Kelly

CHOOSE YOUR OWN OZ

A full-length comedy by
Tommy Jamerson

www.youthplays.com
info@youthplays.com
424-703-5315

COPYRIGHT RULES TO REMEMBER

CAST OF CHARACTERS

NIGEL DEE NARRATOR, male, the show's narrator and audience participation guru. He is omnipresent throughout the course of the show and often provides the audience with his own personal commentary. With this character, ad-libbing is not only suggested but encouraged.

DOROTHY, female, the heroine of today's tale.

TOTO, male, Dorothy's beloved pet.

GLINDA, female, The Good Witch of the South (can double as Mumbi).

MUMBI, female, The One-Eyed Wicked Witch of the West (can double as Glinda).

JACK THE SCARECROW, male, a walking, talking scarecrow who longs for a brain.

TINKER THE TIN MAN, male, a walking, talking tin man who longs for a heart.

EUGENE THE LION, male, a walking, talking, anthropomorphic lion who longs for courage.

THE WIZARD OF OZ, male, The Wizard Himself.

ANNOUNCER

UNCLE HENRY

AUNT EM

THE CYCLONE

THE MAID

THE MUNCHKINS OF MUNCHKINLAND

THE WITCH'S FLYING HENCHMEN

THE TREES OF THE FORBIDDEN FOREST

...and the numerous STAGEHANDS called onstage to aid in moving the plot along. Overall cast size can range from 10-30+ actors.

SCENE-BY-SCENE BREAKDOWN

ACT I

SCENE 1: A BARE STAGE – Nigel, Announcer

SCENE 2: KANSAS – Nigel, Dorothy, Toto, Aunt Em, Uncle Henry, Tornado

SCENE 3: MUNCHKINLAND – Nigel. Dorothy, Toto, Glinda, Munchkins

SCENE 4: THE ROAD TO OZ – Nigel, Dorothy, Toto, Jack, Mumbi, The Trees

SCENE 5: THE FOREBODING FOREST – Nigel, Dorothy, Toto, Jack, The Trees, Tinker

SCENE 6: MUMBI'S LAIR – Nigel, Mumbi, Dorothy, Tinker, Jack, Toto, Flying Monkey, Flying Pig, Flying Ponkey

ACT II

SCENE 1: THE EDGE OF THE FOREST – Nigel, Announcer, Cheetah, Koala, Elephant, Crow, Eugene, Dorothy, Tinker, Jack, Toto

SCENE 2: THE POPPY FIELD – Nigel, Dorothy, Eugene, Tinker, Jack, Toto, The Poppies, Glinda

SCENE 3: OUTSIDE THE GATES OF THE EMERALD CITY – Nigel, Dorothy, Eugene, Tinker, Jack, Toto, Mumbi, The Monkeys

SCENE 4: MUMBI'S TORTURE CHAMBER – Nigel, The Palace Guards, Dorothy, Mumbi, Toto, Monkeys, Jack, Tinker, Eugene

SCENE 5: THE WIZARD'S THRONE ROOM – Nigel, Dorothy, Toto, Jack, Tinker, Eugene, The Great and Powerful Oz

PRODUCTION NOTE

Your production may update the Djimon Hounsou reference as needed.

For my Mother, who first escorted me to Oz.

ACT I

SCENE 1: A BARE STAGE

(A large chair rests comfortably on an otherwise bare stage. Classical music wafts in the background.)

ANNOUNCER: *(Voiceover:)* Ladies and gentlemen, girls and boys of all ages, we'd like to welcome you to tonight's performance of *The Wizard of Oz*! A few things to keep in mind during the show: talking, jumping, dancing, singing, laughing, and interacting with the cast and crew is highly...encouraged! Also, if you see a Wicked Witch anywhere near the premises, feel free to boo her till your heart's content! Now, let's give a big warm welcome to this evening's master of ceremonies, our numero uno storyteller himself; Mister Nigel Dee Narrator!

(Applause. Silence. A cricket chirping can be heard...)

Um...Nigel? Nigel?

NIGEL: *(Off:)* Wait? Is that me?! Am I on already? Oh, me! Oh my! I'm coming everybody! I'm coming!

(NIGEL makes his entrance by running through the audience and up on stage. Perhaps he ad-libs a few "hellos" here and there.)

I'm coming, I'm coming, I'm coming, I'm coming, I'm...whew! I'm here! Jeez-O-Pete I don't think I've run that fast since...well since ever. Anyway, hello out there. How is everybody doing? *(Waits for response.)* We can do better than that! I said "How is everyone doing?" *(Waits again. Feeding off their hopefully positive reaction:)* Good! Good! Well, like they already said, my name is Nigel Dee Narrator and, like my name suggests, I'm a real, live, 100% official Storyteller! See!

(He shows off an official badge. Canned "oohs" and "ahhhs.")

Impressive, right? Anyhoo, today I am going to tell you the tale of a girl named Dorothy, her dog Toto, and of course, the Wonderful Wizard of Oz. All I need now is my light little storybook... Ah! There it is! And we can get—

(The storybook is anything but light or little. He attempts to lift it...)

And we can get...

(Again, another failed attempt. In a strained voice:)

And...we...can...get...

(Falling back into the chair with the book, he lands with a thud!)

Started! You'd think with as many times as I've told this story I'd get used to how heavy it is. I really should've brought Cliff's notes instead but, then again, I haven't seen him in forever.

(Ba Dum Bum. He cackles at this. Crickets again.)

ANYWAY, let's dim the lights...get nice and cozy... And begin!

(He stretches and yawns loudly.)

Pardon me. Okay, page one, chapter one, sentence one. "Dorothy Gale, our story's heroine, lived in... *(Slowly beginning to fall asleep:)* Lived in... Dorothy lived in... *(And he's out.)* Kan... Zzzzzzzzz.

ANNOUNCER: *(Voiceover:)* Psst...Nigel, it's happened again! You've fallen asleep onstage AGAIN! Nigel! NIGEL!

NIGEL: *(With a start, to audience:)* "DOROTHY LIVED IN KANSAS!" Who? Huh? Did I fall asleep onstage? Not again! This is the third time this week! I'm sorry guys, but to be honest with ya, being a narrator can get kinda boring after a while—we tell the same story over and over again. There are no surprises, no excitement. If only there was some way to change things up, and make what once seemed stale and routine, fresh and new again... HEY! I've got an idea! How about you guys help me out tonight? How about I start narrating like normal, BUT every time we stumble upon something that seems stuffy or boring, or that we've seen a thousand times before, I'll blow this whistle right here... *(Producing one from around his neck:)* ...and then we'll all shout "PAUSE" together—Okay, say it with me... *(He blows the whistle.)* PAUSE!—beautiful, and once the story has been paused we can come up with new ideas on how to change things around. How does that sound? Do you want to help decide what happens right here onstage? *(Waits for response.)* Terrific! Okay, I am energized, I am caffeinated, I am ready! Now where was I? Oh, yes... "Dorothy Gale lived in Kansas..."

SCENE 2: KANSAS

CHOOSE YOUR OWN TOTO

(The lights grow dim as a hushed silence falls around the theatre. A quaint farmhouse rests stage right. Suddenly magical notes are played as DOROTHY appears. Pigtails dangle by her ears, and a gingham apron adorns her waist. Eat your heart out, Judy Garland.)

DOROTHY: *(Taking in her surroundings:)* Ah, Kansas... *(Taking a big whiff and addressing the audience:)* You guys should see it; sunny green pastures, bright blue horizons, and— *(Stepping in something grotesque, though she remains cheerful:)* freshly baked cow pies as far as the eye can see. It's gorgeous!

NIGEL: "She happily resided there on a rural little farm with her Uncle Henry and her Aunt Em, both of whom she loved very much."

DOROTHY: It's true, I do.

(HENRY and EM enter, hard at work, as Dorothy blows them a kiss. They both catch it and merrily put the kiss in their respective pockets. Dorothy laughs at this.)

NIGEL: "Dorothy also loved her little black dog Toto, and other than her family, it was he who brought the most joy to her life."

DOROTHY: *(Whistling:)* Oh Toto, where are you boy? There you are. Come here, boy! Come here!

(TOTO, an actor dressed as a little dog, comes yapping in from offstage and runs into Dorothy's awaiting arms. She nuzzles him as the two also share a moment.)

My, what a good puppy you are! Yes, you are. Yes, you are!

NIGEL: Touching moment, isn't it guys? Hmmm... I don't know about you, but I get kinda bored with the whole Dorothy/Dog idea. Say, I know! Why don't we make the first change right here and now? What do you say? Are you with me? *(Waits for their reaction.)* Okay! Wait for my signal and...

(Nigel pulls out his whistle and dangles it for a few seconds.)

DOROTHY: I love my life here so much, Toto! In fact, it makes me want to sing!

(She opens her mouth, perhaps music swells and... Nigel blows the whistle.)

NIGEL: *(With the crowd:)* PAUSE!!!

DOROTHY: Wait—pause?

(Toto cocks his head in confusion.)

NIGEL: Just for a second. See I think the audience and I just want to change one minor thing.

DOROTHY: Oh. All right...I guess. And that is...?

NIGEL: Toto.

DOROTHY: Toto?

(Toto growls.)

NIGEL: Easy boy!

DOROTHY: And what's wrong with Toto?

NIGEL: Nothing! We all love him, but after the first hundred times or so of hearing this story, we can't help but wonder what *The Wizard of Oz* would look like if you had another pet. Something else. Something different. Something *mysterious...*

DOROTHY: But I don't want something *mysterious*, I want something *Toto!*

NIGEL: Look, I tell you what; to make it fair, why don't we take it to a vote?

(Nigel asks the audience to show him what they want Toto to be, either by a raise of hands, or by calling out numbers – 1 for DOG, 2 for SOMETHING ELSE.)

*SCENARIO 1: IF TOTO STAYS A DOG

NIGEL: And it looks like he's going to stay a dog!

DOROTHY: *(Wrapping her arms around her pooch:)* Thank heavens!

TOTO: Bark! Bark!

NIGEL: All right then, where were we? Oh yes!

*SCENARIO 2: IF TOTO TURNS INTO SOMETHING ELSE

NIGEL: It looks like the Something Elsers have it! Sorry Toto, but you're no longer going to be a dog.

DOROTHY: *(Over Toto's whimpers:)* Oh fiddle!

NIGEL: You're instead going to be a...be a... *(It hits him.)* I've got! Instead, you're going to be a COW!

DOROTHY: Really?

(Nigel pulls out a pair of udders. Toto is clearly irritated by this.)

NIGEL: Go on now, try them on.

(Toto does as he's told.)

You look...*udderly* adorable! Doesn't he, folks? Let's try this again from the top! "Dorothy also loved her big moo cow Toto and, other than her family, it was he who brought the most joy to her life."

DOROTHY: Come here, Toto...come here.

TOTO: *(In a deep, raspy voice:)* Mooooo!

(*Playwright's note: Let it be known that in other productions of this show, directors have chosen to instead make Toto other animals such as a chicken, a hen, or even a goat. If you'd prefer to give the audience the option to make him something other than a cow or a dog, I give you full permission. Just change the barks and/or moos to clucks or neighs, and the rest should follow smoothly.)

*END OF CHOSEN SCENARIO

(The play continues on from here. If Toto is a cow, replace the barks with moos, and so on.)

NIGEL: "In fact, it was safe to assume that Dorothy loved pretty much everything about her home; everything, that is, except the occasional, yet highly unpredictable" —

NIGEL/DOROTHY: Twister!

DOROTHY: Oh Toto, Audience, I'm so worried. I overheard Uncle Henry telling Aunt Em that some people are speculating there's going to be the occasional, yet highly unpredictable, twister visiting these very parts this very afternoon! See —

(Lights up on Henry and Em.)

HENRY: Em, some people are speculating that there's going to be a twister visiting these very parts this very afternoon!

EM: Ahhh! Oh no!

DOROTHY: Ahh! Oh no!

(She quakes in her farm boots a bit too loudly and hides under her apron.)

EM: Dorothy Gale, were you eavesdropping again?

DOROTHY: No, Aunt Em, I wasn't. *(Whispering to Toto:) Psst! I totally was.*

EM: And Dorothy Gale, did you remember to lock up your window panes like I told ya?

DOROTHY: Yes, Aunt Em, I did. *(Whispering to Toto:) Psst! I totally didn't!* Poor Aunt Em and Uncle Henry, what'll happen to them if a cyclone comes and ruins the farm? Gasp! And just think Toto, what'll happen to us?!

TOTO: Bark?

DOROTHY: I know, I'm scared too, but that's why we have to stick together, no matter what! Here, I'll keep you safe in my basket.

(Dorothy pulls out a teeny tiny basket. Whether or not Toto is a dog, there's no way anyone, especially said actor, is fitting in the basket. They share a beat.)

Or maybe I'll just keep an eye on you.

NIGEL: "It was then that suddenly, and without...much warning...a cyclone that was half as big as Kansas itself—and about twice as wide as its inhabitants—billowed forth onto the scene and made its way towards Dorothy's farm!"

(The lights flicker, the winds howl, and the TWISTER appears! How you choose to stage this monstrosity is up to you, dear director. Perhaps music underscores.)

DOROTHY: Oh no, Toto! Look! The twister! It's a'comin'! It's a'comin'!

TOTO: Bark-bark! Bark-bark!

DOROTHY: Let's run! Run!

(Dorothy and Toto run comically in place. As they run, bits of farm equipment and such begin to swirl around them — perhaps maneuvered by the stagehands. Dorothy and Toto do their best to dodge the flying debris. Em and Henry approach a storm cellar.)

EM/HENRY: *(In slow motion voices:)* Dor-o-thy! Dor-o-thy!

DOROTHY: We're coming, you two! We're coming! Oh, Toto, we keep running, and running, and yet, we're not getting anywhere!

(The Twister, after a moment, begins to catch up to them.)

Run faster! Faster! Faster!! Fast—

(SLAM! Dorothy's head is suddenly whacked by a flying piece of her window.)

And goodnight, folks!

(She collapses as the scene goes black. Lights remain on Nigel.)

SCENE 3: MUNCHKINLAND
CHOOSE DOROTHY'S FOOTWEAR

NIGEL: THAT was epic! You guys ready for more? "The next morning, Dorothy awoke with a start!"

DOROTHY: Whoa! I'm up with a start!

(Lights rise. Dorothy is in the midst of what appears to be a tiny, enchanted kingdom. She looks left, she looks right, and with all

that looking, she still does not notice her farm house sitting center stage.)

(Groggy:) And oh, my head. I guess forgetting to lock up that window pane wasn't the best idea, eh Toto? ...Toto? *(She jumps to her feet!)* Oh, no! Toto! Where are you, boy?

TOTO: Bark! Bark!

(Toto comes running from behind the house.)

DOROTHY: There you are! Thank goodness you're—Ahhh! Toto! The house! The tornado must've lifted it up and dropped it here with us, but...but the question remains; where *is* here? *(To the audience:)* Do you guys know? Normally I don't like to ask the audience questions, but in this case I have no clue as to where we are or— *(Noticing something under the house:)* Ahh— or what THAT is!

(Lights illuminate two gangly legs sticking out from under the house.)

Omigosh! They're feet! Our house it...it grew feet!

(A high pitched, somewhat overbearing giggle can be heard offstage.)

What—what—what is that?

GLINDA: *(Through giggles, off:)* No need to stutter dear, it's only —

(POOF! GLINDA appears – gliding in on stage.)

ME! DIVA POSE!

(She strikes a diva pose and encourages the audience to applaud.)

Thank you, thank you! How very unexpected. Now tell me child, who are you and—and what is that *creature* doing by your side? He's not a monster, is he? And you're not a wicked witch, are you? ARE YOU?!

DOROTHY: No, I'm Dorothy Gale, of Kansas.

GLINDA: Kan-sas?

DOROTHY: And this is my dog, Toto.

GLINDA: Tutu?

TOTO: Bark-Bark!

GLINDA: How delightful!

DOROTHY: And who are you?

GLINDA: Why I'm Glinda, the oh-so-good and oh-so-gorgeous witch of the South of course!

DOROTHY: I didn't know that witches could be good, or pretty for that matter.

GLINDA: Of course we can be, silly head. I'm beautiful, as all good witches are. Only bad witches are ugly.

NIGEL: "Dorothy was confused by all these recent developments...

(A glazed look overcomes Dorothy's face.)

And her confusion left her with a million questions!"

DOROTHY: It sure has! Like, where are we? And how did we get here?

(Glinda attempts to answer each of Dorothy's questions, but Dorothy won't let her get a word in edgewise as she rambles on at top speed.)

GLINDA: Wel—

DOROTHY: Brought here by the cyclone I supposed. But then if it picked me, my house, and my dog up, why not the rest of my farm?

GLINDA: I'm not—

DOROTHY: Why just us? And where are all the chickens and geese? And where oh where are my Uncle Henry and Aunt Em? Did they make it out alive? I hope they're alive!

GLINDA: I'm s—

DOROTHY: And another thing: since when are witches real? Is this a recent development, or have they been around forever and people are just now learning about them?

GLINDA: Tha—

DOROTHY: And if only bad witches are ugly, which I'm assuming they are since that's what you said and well you're a witch so you'd know, then why did you ask me if was one? Are you saying that I'm ugly? Is that what you're saying? Am I not pretty enough to be a good witch just a—

GLINDA: OKAY, that's enough questions for now! For the purposes of your adventures here, and my sanity, we're going to just move right along and—

DOROTHY: Wait—adventures here? You mean to tell me I'm going on a—

GLINDA: WHAT DID I SAY ABOUT QUESTIONS?

DOROTHY: Sorry.

GLINDA: *(Through giggles:)* It's fine dear, and yes, you are going to go on an adventure—that is, if you ever want to go home again.

DOROTHY: Oh, I do!

GLINDA: Then you're going to have to pay a visit to the Wonderful Wizard of Oz.

MUNCHKINS: *(Off—spoken in voices reminiscent of the Martians in* Toy Story *– "The Claw!")* Oooooh. Ozzzzzzz.

DOROTHY: Oz? That must be where we are, Toto. Oz!

MUNCHKINS: Yesssss. Ozzzzzzzz.

GLINDA: Well, technically you're in Munchkinland, which is on the outskirts of — oh what the heck, yes, for all intents and purposes, you are, in fact, in Oz.

MUNCHKINS: Mmmmm. Ozzzzzzzz.

TOTO: *(Freaked out:)* Bark–Bark!

DOROTHY: I know I'm not supposed to ask any more questions, but — but what is that?

GLINDA: That? Why it's Munchkinland's inhabitants, of course! And just wait till you meet them! *(Clapping her hands and whistling:)* Come on out my babies, it's alright! Come out and meet Dorothy and Tonto!

DOROTHY: That's Toto.

GLINDA: Whatever. Come out, come out wherever you — I SAID "COME OUT!"

(The MUNCHKINS emerge.)

There you are.

DOROTHY: Why they're little people!

GLINDA: We prefer the term "vertically challenged," or "munchkin." *(To the Munchkins:)* Now go on, say "hello!"

(The Munchkins surround Dorothy, tackling her with hugs and kisses. They speak in high pitched voices.)

MUNCKINS: *(Speaking over one another:)* Hello! Hi yah! Howdy!

MUNCHKIN 1: You must forgive us for being shy...

MUNCHKIN 2: But we're in awe of you —

MUNCHKIN 3: And your greatness!

MUNCHKINS: Yessss. Your greatnessss!

DOROTHY: My greatness?

MUNCHKINS: Mmmmhmmmm.

MUNCHKIN 3: Not only did your arrival bring us Glinda the Good —

GLINDA: And beautiful.

MUNCHKIN 1: But you also rescued us from our sworn enemy...

MUNCHKIN 2: The one we liked the least —

MUNCHKIN 3: The one who is deceased —

MUNCHKINS: The Witched Witch of the East!

DOROTHY: Deceased? Witch of the East?

(She realizes and runs over to the house.)

Oh, Toto I was wrong, so very, very wrong! Our house, it didn't grow feet — instead it squished someone else's! Along with the rest of them!

NIGEL: "And Dorothy was right, for indeed, still under the corner of the great beam the house rested on, two feet were sticking out, shod in silver shoes and painted toes. The girl was beside herself, unaware of what to do next."

DOROTHY: I can't believe someone's...dead.

MUNCHKIN 2: As a doornail.

MUNCHKIN 1: Dead. Dead. Dead.

MUNCHKIN 3: And now there's only one thing left to do.

MUNCHKINS: CELEBRATE! *(Showering Dorothy in glitter and confetti:)* Hip-Hurray! Hip-Hurray! Hip-hip —

DOROTHY: Stop! Stop!

MUNCHKIN 1: ...hurray?

DOROTHY: This is horrible! Why, I didn't realize that my house landed on a person!

GLINDA: You didn't? Huh, I must've left that part out. Oh well, on with the festivities!

DOROTHY: No, this isn't right! I squished someone!

GLINDA: That's right you did, and for doing so...YOU'RE GOING TO BE REWARDED!

MUNCHKINS: HURRAY!

DOROTHY: Rewarded for homicidally squishing an innocent bystander? This is awful!

GLINDA: Innocent? *(Laughing heartily:)* My dear, the Witch of the East was a lot of things, but innocent wasn't one of them. Why, she was as wicked as they come...well *almost*. More on that later. She used to terrorize my poor Munchkins, and even worse, force them to speak in whiny, obnoxious, high pitched voices!

MUNCHKIN 1: *(In a horribly high-pitched voice:)* She sure di—

GLINDA: We get it, we get it. *(To Dorothy:)* So you see, Dorothy, you may view yourself as awful, but the Munchkins, why they see you as a hero!

DOROTHY: Then why don't I feel like one?

GLINDA: *(Clapping her hands together:)* You will once you have these little babies on your feet! Munchkins, bring them forth!

MUNCHKINS: Oooooh. Ahhhhhh. Themmmmmm.

GLINDA: Dorothy of Kan-Sas I present to you and your dog Djimon Hounsou the—

DOROTHY: Djimon Hounsou? That doesn't even SOUND like Toto.

GLINDA: Huh. You're right. ANYWAY, from the cold, dead hooves of the Wicked Witch; I give you the famed, the revered, the enchanted—

NIGEL: *(Blowing his whistle:)* And PAUSE!

GLINDA: Pause?

MUNCHKIN 2: Paws?

MUNCHKIN 3: Like an animal's claws?

NIGEL: No, like as it's time to remix this up a bit.

DOROTHY: Not again!

(The cast begins to chatter amongst themselves.)

NIGEL: I know, I know, but hear me out. Audience, usually at this part in the story Dorothy wears what? *(Encouraging the kids to shout "Ruby Slippers" or just "Slippers" in general:)* Slippers! Right! But instead of the same-old, same-old, why don't we give her something new to wear? And that *something new* can be found in... *(He pulls out a glittery bag! Spoken in a booming echo:)* The Magical Bag of Enchantment-ment-ment-ment!

GLINDA: The Bag of what?

NIGEL: Enchantment-ment-ment-ment-ment. It's a special bag that has all sorts of options for Dorothy to try on. What do you say guys? Wanna give it a try? *(Encouraging the audience:)* And what about you, Dorothy? What do you say?

DOROTHY: *(Clearly not happy with this development:)* I say, "Never mess with a girl and her shoes."

NIGEL: C'mon Dorothy, please! *(To audience:)* Help me out here. Please! Please!

DOROTHY: Oh, all right, if it'll make them happy.

NIGEL: Terrific! Listen guys, in order to pull from the Bag of Enchantment, I'm going to need a volunteer from the audience!

> *(A little bit more about the "Magical Bag of Enchantment"; the bag is filled to the brim with folded pieces of paper. The child selected from the audience reaches in and pulls one out. On each piece of paper is a shoe option. There can be as many different shoe options as you like, however, if you're [a.] on a budget or [b.] want to make things easier, I suggest filling those tiny pieces of paper with only two options, the first being the traditional silver slippers found in the book – the ruby ones are copyrighted by Warner Brothers – and the second being hilariously oversized ruby red clown shoes. Silly, yes, but kids will eat it up.)*

*SCENARIO 1: IF SILVER SHOES ARE SELECTED

> *(After Nigel asks the child's name, he allows the child to pull a slip of paper. Assuming there are only two options, in this scenario the child pulls the Silver Shoes piece of paper.)*

NIGEL: And it looks like Dorothy will be wearing...

DOROTHY: *(With eyes closed and crossing her fingers:)* Oh please, oh please, oh please...

NIGEL: ...Silver Slippers this evening!

> *(The Munchkins bring the Silver Shoes forth and present them proudly at Dorothy's feet. She tries them on.)*

DOROTHY: Oh! They fit, they fit—and I look fantastic in them! *(To the volunteer:)* Thank you so much!

NIGEL: Let's give a big round of applause for our volunteer!

> *(Nigel escorts the child back to his/her seat.)*

See, that wasn't so bad.

DOROTHY: No it wasn't!

GLINDA: Now Nigel, please continue with your narration!!

(The scene plays out as is.)

*SCENARIO 2: IF RUBY RED CLOWN SHOES ARE CHOSEN

> *(After Nigel asks the child's name, he allows the child to pull a slip of paper. Assuming there are only two options, in this scenario, the child pulls the Ruby Red Clown Shoe piece of paper. IF, however, you choose to have more options, just alter the words "Ruby Red Clown Shoe" to fit whatever footwear you're presenting Dorothy with. The rest of the lines should follow suit throughout the play.)*

NIGEL: And it looks like Dorothy will be wearing...

DOROTHY: Oh please, oh please, oh please...

NIGEL: ...The Ruby Red...

DOROTHY: Yes!

NIGEL: ...Oversized and Overly Floppy...Clown Shoes!

DOROTHY: What?!

> *(The Munchkins bring the shoes forth and present them proudly at Dorothy's feet. She tries them on. Less than enthusiastic.)*

Oh goodie. They fit.

NIGEL: Let's give a big round of applause for our volunteer!

> *(Nigel escorts the child back to his/her seat and the scene plays out as is.)*

See, that wasn't so bad.

DOROTHY: *(Sarcastically:)* No. Not at all.

GLINDA: Nigel, please continue with your narration!

*END OF CHOSEN SCENARIO

> *(The play continues on from here. If Dorothy's shoes are NOT the silver slippers, replace the lines accordingly.)*

NIGEL: With pleasure! "Dorothy looked ravishing in her new footwear, and tried walking in them as Glinda bestowed her with some much-needed advice."

GLINDA: I hope you're enjoying them; you're going to need to keep them firmly strapped as you make your way to see the Wizard of Oz.

DOROTHY: Really? But why?

GLINDA: Did I forget to tell you? I did! Silly me. Thanks to your little squishing incident, when the Witch of the East's sister, Mumbi, the One-Eyed Witch of the West, learns of what you've done, she's more than likely to hunt you down and well...

(A Bum! Bum! Bum! is cued.)

You get the idea. But, as long as you have those shoes planted tightly on your tootsies, she can't hurt you…much.

DOROTHY: Another evil witch! *(To the audience:)* This sounds like more than I bargained for!

GLINDA: Trust me, it is. But you'll be fine! Just follow the Yellow Brick Road and you'll make it to the Wizard in a cinch. And, if you encounter any dangers along the way, use this...

(Glinda kisses her hand and places it on Dorothy's forehead.)

DOROTHY: A kiss?

GLINDA: A *magic* kiss. With it, you can call upon me if ever you're in need. But use it wisely, I can only be summoned once. Now if you'll excuse me, the Munchkins and I are late for a very important date. Goodbye you two, and good luck!

MUNCHKINS: Goodbye! Goodbye!

DOROTHY: But where are you going? Don't leave! I have so many more questions! About these shoes! And the Wizard!

What does he look like? How will I know him when I find him?

GLINDA: Nobody knows for certain what he looks like — he's a mystery to us all. But that said, I'm sure, deep down, you'll know him in your heart of hearts when you see him. Now, Ta-Ta, dear! TA-TA! And good luck in Oz!

MUNCHKINS: Ooooooh. Ozzzzzzzz.

DOROTHY: No! Wait I —

GLINDA: DIVA OUT!

(POOF! She disappears, along with the Munchkins! Beat.)

TOTO: Bark-Bark.

DOROTHY: I know, Toto...she really IS a diva, whatever that is. Anyway, I guess all there is to do now is follow the Yellow Brick Road. But where is the —

(Lights shine down, revealing the road. Harmonious notes are played.)

Oh, there it is! Let's follow it Toto, and find this Wonderful Wizard! The faster we walk, the faster we'll get home!

(Dorothy and Toto follow the road and exit as the lights begin to dim.)

SCENE 4: THE ROAD TO OZ

NIGEL: "That afternoon, Dorothy and Toto merrily made their way through Oz. They passed many strange towns and dwellings, and even passed a few gargantuan plants, the likes of which they'd never seen before. As the day pressed on, Dorothy and her furry friend began to grow weary, but they knew that only in persevering would they reach the Wizard in a timely fashion. And so they continued to walk...and walk...AND WALK...AND —

(Dorothy and Toto enter, hunched over and bathed in sweat from their long and exhausting journey. Perhaps both their tongues are dangling from their mouths. JACK, a scarecrow, sits off in the distance.)

DOROTHY: *(Out of breath:)* Jiminy Crickets, Toto! I never realized the Wizard's house was so far away, did you?

(Toto shakes his head "no.")

In fact, I never realized that a road could be so long. We must have been walking for...for miles!

JACK: To be exact; that is if you're coming from Munchkinland.

DOROTHY: *(Gasp!)* What was that?

NIGEL: "Dorothy searched and searched, but she couldn't tell where the mysterious voice was coming from."

DOROTHY: I surely cannot. *(To the audience:)* Did you see anything?

(Jack creeps up behind them...)

NIGEL: "Then suddenly, without warning..."

DOROTHY: Toto, do you hear—?

(Jack taps Dorothy on the back...)

JACK: Hello!

DOROTHY/TOTO: Ahhh!

JACK: Ahhh!

DOROTHY/TOTO: Ahhh!

DOROTHY/TOTO/JACK: Ahhhhh!

JACK: Wait everyone! Wait! Why are we screaming?

DOROTHY: Because you're a walking, talking scarecrow! That's why!

JACK: That's true, I am. Continue on then...

DOROTHY: Thank you. *(With Toto:)* Ahhhh...

JACK: You better now? Now that you got that out?

DOROTHY: Yes, much. Now tell me; who are you and how are you able to talk?

JACK: The name's Jack, at least, I think it is. To be honest I'm not sure. And as far as why I'm able to communicate with you...or communicate period...huh...I'm not sure I'm sure about that one either.

DOROTHY: You're not?

JACK: Nope.

DOROTHY: Well what kind of person...err scarecrow...knows how to talk, but isn't sure how it's plausible?

JACK: Sadly, the kind that doesn't have a brain. I mean, sure, the farmer that stuffed me gave me straw and hay to spare but, at the end of the day, when he went inside to deal with a personal matter, he forgot about my cerebral matter! Now I ask you, what's a scarecrow to do?

DOROTHY: That IS tricky. Say, I know! Even though we just met and you're kinda creepy, why don't you join me in my quest to meet the Wizard of Oz? I'm going to ask him to send me back home to Kansas. If he can do that, maybe he can give you a brain!

JACK: That's genius! Why didn't I think of that? ...Oh, right. But wait, how will we ever find this Wizard?

DOROTHY: According to Glinda, if we just keep following this Yellow Brick Road, we'll be at the Wizard's in no time!

JACK: That's stupendous! Oh, thank you ah, ah...

DOROTHY: Dorothy Gale; and this is my dog, Toto.

TOTO: Bark-Bark!

JACK: Nice to meet you both!

DOROTHY: You, too, Jack. Now what are we waiting for? Let's go!

JACK: Oh boy, let's! In fact, let's run!

DOROTHY: No, let's skip!

JACK: No, let's —

MUMBI: *(Voiceover:)* NOT! SO! FAST!

> *(POOF! In a cloud of smoke, MUMBI, the Witch of the West appears...and coughs. A black eye patch rests over her left eye as she continues to hack up her lungs for a moment. Once finished, she wipes the smoke away and takes a menacing step forward.)*

NIGEL: And here comes the character I like least — our story's villain, Mumbi the One-Eyed Wicked Witch of the West.

> *(Bum! Bum! Bum!)*

Feel free to boo. Boo! Boo!

MUMBI: Enough! *Sooo*, this is the little out-of-towner who thought she could just drop in my land and drop a house on my sister! Bet you think you're pretty clever, don't you?

DOROTHY: No-no-no, ma'am! I don't think I'm clever at all!

MUMBI: That's good, because you're not! My poor departed sister may have been blind to your tricks, but ol' Mumbi here won't be fooled so easily. Now, before I do away with you and your brainless friend here--

JACK: — That hurts me.

MUMBI: Hand over those enchanted shoes!

DOROTHY: *(If wearing the clown shoes:)* Believe me, I wish I could — but Glinda told me not to! *(If wearing the silver shoes:)* Never! Glinda told me not to.

JACK: That's right!

TOTO: Bark-bark!

JACK: Psst, what's a Glinda?

MUMBI: Never you mind that! I should've known she'd just pawn off my family's most prized possession on someone else without even consulting me first! She's rude that way, you know.

DOROTHY: Huh, you're right, that IS rude.

MUMBI: I know! But no matter, I'll just take them by force then!

(Mumbi lunges at Dorothy's feet, and, as a result of touching the enchanted shoes, is electrocuted!)

Ahhh! They electrocuted me! Maybe if I try again...

(Again, it happens.)

Ahhh! Well, mother always said "persistence is a virtue!"

(Again, it happens.)

Ahhhhhh! It's no use.

NIGEL: "Yes the witch tried and tried to release Dorothy's grip from the enchanted shoes, but no matter how many times she attempted they would not come off. Finally, after the fourth try —"

MUMBI: Fourth try?

NIGEL: That's what it says here.

MUMBI: Ugh.

NIGEL: "And finally, after the FOURTH try..."

MUMBI: FINE! *(She attempts and fails. Releasing an almost operatic yelp:)* AHHHHHHHHHHH!!!

NIGEL: "...she realized that the power of the shoes far outweighed her own."

MUMBI: *(Mimicking him:) She realized that the power of the shoes far outweighed her own.* Of course I realized that! I could've told you that THREE tries ago! But, no matter! Unfortunately for me, these darlings will never come off, not as long as you're breathing! But unfortunately for you, THAT is something that I can remedy!

(The Witch begins to cackle incessantly and takes another step towards Dorothy when –)

Ow! Ow! What is this?

(She picks up a rotten apple – during her laughing spree two of them were chucked directly at her.)

Ouch! An apple? What's an apple doing –

(A few more come hurling at her.)

Ow! Ow! Stop! What's going on?

(The sound of rustling and heavy footsteps can be heard as three large, mobile TREES step forward – moldy, rotten apples hanging from their limbs.)

DOROTHY: Scarecrow, look! The trees – they're moving!

MUMBI: Trees?

TREE 1: That's right, Witch. Trees! And unless you want another one of our juicy red apples –

TREE 2: Thrown directly at that ol' kisser of yours –

TREE 1: Then we suggest you leave the girl alone!

MUMBI: *(To audience:)* SERIOUSLY! I'm being threatened by talking trees?

TREE 3: You are, and believe you me, you don't want to mess with us.

TREE 1: No, ma'am!

TREE 2: 'Cause pardon the expression, but our bark really IS worse than our bite!

(They strike a threatening pose and let out a grunt!)

TREE 3: So what's it gonna be, Witch?!

(The Trees, each holding an apple in hand...err...branch...get into position, ready to attack.)

TREES: *(All:)* Well?

MUMBI: I'll go. There's no need for blood or apple-shed today, gentlemen. But know this, *Dorothy*; this little altercation is far from over. Oh no! I'll be back! *(If, and ONLY if, Toto is a cow:)* And when I return, I'll get you my pretty, and your little...not-so-little...kinda-big cow too!

(Smoke billows forth. Again Mumbi cackles, and again she begins to cough.)

I've really gotta give up smoking!

(POOF! She disappears! Dorothy runs up to the Trees in appreciation.)

DOROTHY: Thank you so much!

JACK: Yes, thank you!

TREE 1: It was our pleasure.

TREE 2: It was?

TREE 3: It was! Anyone who wears the Silver Slippers we, the trees of the forest, are sworn to protect.

JACK: Well what do ya know? That Glinda person knew what she was doing after all!

TREE 2: So, while you have many things to fear during your trek through The Foreboding Forest of Forbidden Fruit, know this—we trees are not one of them.

DOROTHY: Wait, wait, wait... The Foreboding Forest of Forbidden Fruit?

TREE 2: You're following the Yellow Brick Road, aren't you?

JACK: Not if it means passing through a deep, dark forest we're not.

TREE 3: But you must—it's the only way to reach the Wizard! See...

(A sign appears. Dorothy and Jack read it in unison.)

DOROTHY/JACK: "Welcome To The Foreboding Forest of Forbidden Fruit—AKA—The Only Way To Reach The Wizard!"

JACK: We can't go through there!

DOROTHY: Don't be such a cowardly lion, Jack! We have to! Remember, the Wizard is my only way back to Kansas—and your only way to get a brain! Please!

JACK: I hate to admit it, but you're right. Through the forest?

DOROTHY: Through the forest!

TOTO: Bark-Ba-Bark!

(The group, including some, if not all the Trees, proceeds with caution as they enter the dark abyss.)

SCENE 5: THE FOREBODING FOREST
OF FORBIDDEN FRUIT

(Dorothy, Jack, Toto and the Trees walk in place as the lights shift around them. Eerie sounds are heard as branches break and crows caw.)

NIGEL: *(Speaking in almost a whisper as if telling a ghost story:)* "The trio made their way through the thicket of the forest, surrounded by darkness. The road before them was still paved with yellow brick, but it was much covered by dried branches and dead leaves from the Trees, who, as luck would have it, stomped alongside our heroes in hopes of shielding them from whatever tricks Mumbi might have up her sleeve. As they marched onward, they continued to hear the strangest of sounds —

(A sound can be heard offstage.)

The sounds it seemed were growing louder...

(The sound again.)

And louder...

(Again!)

Until finally..."

(AGAIN!!!)

TREE 2: I CAN'T TAKE IT ANYMORE! What is it?! WHAT IS IT?

TREE 3: *(Calming his nerves:)* It's nothing, Tree Number Two. Now calm down.

TINKER: *(Off:)* He's right. It's nothing. Only...

(TINKER appears — axe in hand)

A simple tin woodsman!

(The group lets out a sign of relief.)

TREE 1: Wait... Woodsman? As in the axe-carrying kind?

TINKER: That'd be me!

(The Trees scream in panic and begin to run in circles.)

TREE 3: Come on, guys! We gotta get outta here!

JACK: But wait! I thought you were sworn to protect us!

TREE 2: Against witches? Yes. Against branch-trimming axes? Heck no!

TREE 1: You're on your own now!

TREE 3: Let's get out of here, guys—I'm shaking like a leaf!

TREES: Good luck, Dorothy!!

DOROTHY: Wait! Please wait! *(Beat.)* Son of a Birch!

NIGEL: "The trees fled for their lives, leaving in their wake our very confused heroes and an animated Tin Man."

TINKER: That's Tinker, the animated Tin Man.

NIGEL: My apologies.

TINKER: No problem. Now how can I be of service to you?

DOROTHY: Service? All you've done is do us a DISservice!

TINKER: Really? But, how?

JACK: By scaring the trees off! They were our only protection from the Witch of the West you...you...hollow...heartless... axe-wielding menace!

(Tinker begins to cry. He pulls out a hanky.)

DOROTHY: Jack, I think he's crying.

JACK: Look pal, I didn't mean to—

TINKER: No, when you're right, you're right—and you're right. I am heartless, heartless as they come...

JACK: No you're not.

TINKER: No, I am, literally...HEARTLESS!

(He pounds on his chest, a hollow thud greets him in return.)

And now, thanks to all these waterworks, I'm gonna... I'm gonna... I'm gonna rust.

(He cries even more, then, almost instantaneously, rusts. Spoken through gritted, and rusted, teeth.)

See.

DOROTHY: Poor Tinker. We should help him. But, how?

JACK: Gee whiz, I don't know. That's a real head scratcher. If only we knew what he was saying.

TINKER: *(Still spoken through gritted teeth:)* Oil can. Get. My. Oil Can.

JACK: *(To audience:)* What about you, out there? Do you know what he said?

TINKER: Oil. Can.

DOROTHY: Marzipan?

JACK: No that doesn't sound right.

TINKER: Oil. Can.

DOROTHY: Handyman, maybe?

JACK: No, no. *(It hits him!)* I've got it! How about Peter Pan?

TINKER: Oil! Can! Oil! Can!

DOROTHY/JACK: *(Reacting off the audience:)* Oh! OIL CAN!

DOROTHY: And look Jack, there's one right here!

(Dorothy scoops it up and begins oiling.)

What should we do first?

TINKER: My neck, please!

NIGEL: "So Dorothy oiled it, and as it was quite badly rusted the Scarecrow took hold of the tin head and moved it gently from side to side —"

TINKER: He said gently!

JACK: Sorry!

NIGEL: "And finally he was able to move freely."

TINKER: *(With a big sigh of relief:)* Ahhh, thank you.

DOROTHY/JACK: You're welcome.

TOTO: Bark-bark!

TINKER: I'm sorry for scaring off your only protection from the Wicked Witch. Believe me, I know just how wicked she can be! Why she's the very reason I'm standing in front of you right now.

DOROTHY: She is?

TINKER: Yes, ma'am. See she built me years ago in the hope that I would chop down all the trees in this here forest! Why, she even removed my heart to make doubly sure that I wouldn't have any remorse about doing it. But heart or no heart, I just couldn't harm another living thing. Something about it just didn't sit right with me.

DOROTHY: Good for you, Tinker!

TINKER: *(Beginning to tear up:)* Thanks, now if only the Witch had been that supportive. She was so angry with me that she abandoned me; left me here to wander these woods for the rest of eternity with nothing but my axe, my oil can...and my loneliness. Dorothy, could you get the oil can ready? I feel another sob session coming on.

DOROTHY: Of course.

(She oils his tear ducts.)

TINKER: Thank you.

JACK: Poor guy, if only there were something we could do for him. Say Dorothy!

(He whispers loudly, but inaudibly, in Dorothy's ear.)

DOROTHY: Uh huh...uh huh...uh yes! I completely agree. Say Tinker, we have a proposition for you.

TINKER: You do?

NIGEL: "And so Dorothy and Jack asked the Tin Man to join their little party. 'After all,' they thought, 'if this great wizard was powerful enough to send her back to Kansas, and to plop a few brains in the Scarecrow's head, then it stood to reason that giving Tinker a heart wouldn't be a challenge in the least.' Tinker was overjoyed—"

TINKER: YES! I'd love to come!

NIGEL: "...and happily accepted their invitation."

TINKER: This is hands down the sweetest thing anybody's ever done for me! In fact, I think I'm gonna cry...again!

DOROTHY/JACK/TOTO: *(Overlapping   one   another:)* No!/No!/Bark!

JACK: Not again!

DOROTHY: And not now! We've got to get a move on!

TINKER: *(Extending his arm:)* You're right Dorothy, Scarecrow, furry animal thingy—no time like the present! Shall we?

DOROTHY: We shall.

(The group locks arms and continues off into the forest.)

NIGEL: "And they were off again, trekking even closer to the Wizard and his magnificent palace made of emeralds."

SCENE 6: MUMBI'S LAIR
CHOOSE YOUR OWN MONSTER

NIGEL: "Unfortunately for them, at another castle — one made of brimstone and coal — one beady eye was watching. This of course was the home of — "

MUMBI: *(Off:)* SILENCE, NARRATOR!

(POOF! Mumbi appears! Again she hacks as she wipes the smoke away.)

I can do my OWN entrances, thank you very much.

NIGEL: Fine. If that's the way you want to play it, I won't say another word then.

MUMBI: Good.

NIGEL: Good. *(To audience:)* Psst — if you feel like booing, this would be a great time to do so.

(He encourages the children to boo once more.)

MUMBI: *(Silencing the children:)* Enough! Enough! This, dear children, is my home sweet home, filled to the brim with skeletons and sorcery! Isn't it just wonderfully wretched? Now if you'll excuse me, I need to see what those loathsome do-gooders are up to!

(She pulls out a spyglass and looks through it. Dorothy, Jack, Tinker, and Toto appear stage left, walking in place.)

Why, they've almost reached the end of the forest! Curses! How can their heads be so slow, but their feet so fast? I've got to send something after them, but what? Wait a minute, I know; you audience members have been helping Dorothy on her little quest all along, haven't you? Yes. Well, now things are going to change because this witch has an idea and it involves YOU helping ME!

(Mumbi snaps her fingers and lights fade on Dorothy and the group.)

Oh, Narrator...

NIGEL: Yes, Mumbi?

MUMBI: I demand a pause! Well, go on now, blow that little whistle of yours! C'mon!

NIGEL: Nice try. Listen—do me a favor, okay? I'm gonna take a nap here, and, when your whole monologuing spiel is over, wake me up so I can get back to the good stuff. Man, am I beat.

MUMBI: *(Laughing:)* Oh Narrator, you're so funny, you know that? *So* funny. But do you know what's even funnier? Me turning this audience and all these *precious* children into toads if you don't pucker up and blow and PAUSE THIS SHOW!

NIGEL: You wouldn't. You're bluffing!

MUMBI: Am I? Only one way to find out!

(She pulls out a wand and aims it at the audience.)

NIGEL: But Mumbi, turning the audience into amphibians just because you didn't get your way that's—that's just bad manners.

MUMBI: Fortunately for me, those are the only kind of manners I like. Well?!? What's it going to be, Narrator?!

NIGEL: Ah...I...I'm sorry guys, but she's right. We don't have any other choice. Say it with me now!

(He blows.)

PAUSE!

MUMBI: Excellent! Now sweet children, I'm going to give you three options, three creatures that, when unleashed, will hunt down Dorothy and her friends and put an end to their escapades once and for all! Your first choice is my oh-so-evil, oh-so-useful...FLYING MONKEY!

(A FLYING MONKEY enters.)

Hello, my baby. The second monster is a creation of mine that the Wizard himself told me would work only when pigs fly! Fortunately for me, they now do! You all should run, you all should have fear, because my FLYING PIG IS HERE!

(A FLYING PIG enters.)

And for your third option, I've decided to bring out something very special — a beast with the arms of a monkey, the nose of a pig, and the wings of a bat! For your delight and delectation, I give you...my FLYING PONKEY, half pig and half monkey!

(A FLYING PONKEY emerges.)

Which will it be? The decision is up to YOU! Time to vote! Narrator, you keep track.

(Mumbi gets the audience to raise their hands and vote for which monster they want her to send out. Nigel keeps score. Whichever monster the audience selects, the following dialogue should still work.)

(To the creature selected:) What a fiendishly fabulous choice — and my personal favorite!!

(A chorus of roars can be heard offstage.)

NIGEL: Oh no, what — what's that?

MUMBI: Why, my winged soldiers, of course! Come forth, my babies, come forth!

(The Monkeys come forth!)

NIGEL: Oh no! Oh no, oh no, oh no!

MUMBI: Excellent! *(To one of the winged beasts:)* My fine feathered friends, rally all your brothers and sisters, and when

I give the signal, hunt that little farm girl down and her obnoxious little friends too!

NIGEL: But wait! You can't do that! What's going to happen to them?

MUMBI: Oh, you'll find out—but not until AFTER I cast my greatest curse of all—intermission!

NIGEL: No! Not intermission! Anything but that! Anything but—

MUMBI: *(Waving her wand:)* It's too late, Narrator! It's already started—see!

(The lights begin to dim, perhaps music underscores.)

NIGEL: No, not this! But we're smack dab in the middle of the story! It's not time for a break, it's not time to—to—to go to the bathroom!

MUMBI: Oh, but it is! It is! It's time to do all that—AND MORE! We'll see you in fifteen, folks!

(Mumbi cackles gleefully as the curtain comes crashing down! Intermission!)

ACT II

SCENE 1: THE EDGE OF THE FOREST

(Lights rise on Nigel, weeping bitterly into a hanky, surrounded by piles and piles of used, scrunched-up Kleenex.)

NIGEL: No, no! Not intermission! Anything but intermission! I just can't stand it when a play calls for an inter—

ANNOUNCER: *(Voiceover:)* Um, Nigel...

NIGEL: Mission?

ANNOUNCER: *(Voiceover:)* We're back.

NIGEL: We are? *(Notices audience:)* Great Scott, we are! Thank you!

ANNOUNCER: *(Voiceover:)* You're welcome! And my name's Peter.

(Or whatever name you want to give the announcer.)

NIGEL: Thank heavens that's over with! And look, the audience, you all came back! You're here! Well...most of you anyway.

(He laughs a little and then blows his nose loudly.)

As you can see, I might've gotten a little carried away here. No matter; you're here, I'm here, and that awful Mumbi is gone! Whew! Anyhoo, now's as good a time as any to move ahead with the second part of our story. Don't you agree?

(Waits for response, flipping through his book.)

Fantastic! Now where were we? Oh, that's right; they were still in the forest. And a few yellow steps ahead of our comrades a herd of animals had gathered.

(A few animals—a CHEETAH, a CROW, a KOALA, and an ELEPHANT—enter, all conversing with one another.)

"Roaring their roars and squawking their squawks, the animals were complaining about something horrible, something awful, something that, they felt, was even more disturbing than the wicked witch herself." ...Me personally I can't imagine ANYTHING being worse than a wicked witch, but—

CHEETAH: You can't? Try having a *wimp* for a *king!*

ANIMALS: *Yeah, yeah!*

CROW: That'll change your tune.

NIGEL: Really?

ELEPHANT: Believe me, it's terrible!

CROW: Ghastly!

KOALA: And pretty much UnBEARable!

(He laughs at his own remark. The other animals ignore him and carry on.)

CHEETAH: It's settled then! We've got to do something!

ANIMALS: *Yeah! Yeah!*

ELEPHANT: Something like finding new king!

CROW: Someone better!

CHEETAH: Someone fearless!

KOALA: And someone who isn't so ImPAWsible!

CHEETAH: Then let it be known far and wide that we, the animals of Oz, are sick and tired of being ruled by a guy that's such a fraidy cat, that can't even stand up to his own shadow, let alone the evils that lurk in these here woods.

ANIMALS: You got that right!/I agree!

ELEPHANT: And unless our king starts acting less like a mouse and more like a man eater, it's gonna be time to elect a new one!

ANIMALS: *HEAR! HEAR!*

CROW: And for those of you out there, Dear Audience, who aren't familiar with whom we're referencing...

CHEETAH: We present to you our fearful leader.

CROW: The one,

ELEPHANT: The only,

KOALA: And the totally UnKOALAfied —

(The animals pause for a moment and give Koala the once over.)

ELEPHANT: ...Really?

KOALA: Yeah. That was lame even for me.

(Cheetah clears her throat and they continue.)

ANIMALS: Eugene the Cowardly Lion.

(EUGENE is revealed, shaking and shivering behind a bush.)

EUGENE: Ohhh! I just hate entrances! I really, really do! Then again, I'm also not a fan of exits either! Ohhh, it's all on account of my stage fright, don'cha know?!

ANIMALS: Stage fright?

EUGENE: Yeah, which makes my decision to participate in today's show questionable to say the least.

KOALA: I'll say.

CHEETAH: Listen, Eugene, be that as it may, your loyal subjects and I have decided that if you don't start acting right —

ELEPHANT: Acting like a lion should,

CHEETAH: Then we're going to have no other choice but to —

CROW: Dethrone you! De-crown you! And, quite possibly, Declaw you as well!

ANIMALS: Yeah/I agree/Here, Here!

EUGENE: Well...that doesn't sound so bad.

ELEPHANT: Not to mention throwing that childish blanket of yours to the wolves!

EUGENE: My blankey! Oh no! Anything but that! Anything but *my precious*!

CHEETAH: We'll give you the night to think it over, but after that we're going to have to take affirmative action. Got it?

EUGENE: Unfortunately.

ANIMALS: Good!

   (The animals begin to exit.)

EUGENE: Leapin' lionesses, what am I gonna do? *(To blanket:)* What are *we* going to do?

KOALA: Don't worry, Eugene — I'm still rootin' for ya.

EUGENE: Thanks, Larry.

KOALA: Anytime. Oh, and if you need anything, make sure you... *(Pulling out a fish:)* Let MINNOW.

   (He laughs at his joke and exits.)

I am too punny.

EUGENE: Balderdash! This would be a lot easier if only I weren't so — so...

NIGEL: Scared?

EUGENE: Ahhhhh! Who was that?

NIGEL: It's me, Nigel — your friendly neighborhood Narrator.

EUGENE: Oh no! I'm terrified of Narrators! At least, I think I am!

(Eugene hides under a bush once more.)

NIGEL: "Poor Eugene, if only he weren't so scared of, well, everything. But, despite his flaws, he was still determined."

EUGENE: I am? That's right, I am!

NIGEL: "He was still a lion!"

EUGENE: Darn tootin'!

NIGEL: "He was still a king!"

EUGENE: I know that's right!

NIGEL: "And, above all else, he was still...he was still..."

EUGENE: ...Yeah?

NIGEL: "He was still...frightened out of his wits."

EUGENE: You said it, brother! But what am I to do? If I want to keep my kingdom and the respect of my subjects, then I've gotta get some...courage.

NIGEL: "And then, just as if Lady Luck herself were intervening, our fantastic foursome from Act One—Dorothy, Toto, Jack, and Tinker—emerged."

(They emerge.)

EUGENE: Dorothy? Toto? Jack and Tinker?! I don't know what, or who, those things are, but I'm positively positive they sound awfully awful! I'd better run! I'd better hide! I'd better—

DOROTHY: Why hello there, Mister Lion. My, what a beautiful coat you have! Tell me, would you like to be friends?

TOTO: Bark! Bark!

EUGENE: I'd Better Get Outta Here!!!

(Eugene screams, runs, and attempts to hide all at the same time. This attempt is anything but successful.)

JACK: Psst...if you ask me, that Lion is a few hairs short of a mane.

TINKER: Agreed.

(Toto laughs at this.)

DOROTHY: Shhh, you three! He's just nervous is all. Poor guy. Why don't we help him? Oh Mister Lion. Mister Cowardly Lion, why are you hiding?

EUGENE: If you must know I'm hiding because the world is a big scary place that expects you to be courageous, noble, and responsible all at the same time, and sadly, I just don't have the patience or the cojones to deal with it. Now go away, please. Can't you see I'm wallowing in self pity? *(To self:)* Oh, if only I were just a tad bit braver, then life wouldn't be so hard. If only.

DOROTHY: Say you guys; what if we asked the lion to come with us? Maybe the Wizard could give him some courage?

JACK: I suppose it's worth a shot.

TINKER: Yeah, as long as he doesn't slow us down.

DOROTHY: He won't, I'm sure of it. Have a heart, Tinker.

(Tinker lowers his head in shame.)

I mean, it'll work out—you'll see! Um, pardon me for interrupting you again, ahh...

EUGENE: Eugene.

DOROTHY: Okay, Eugene, but my friends and I just wanted to extend an invite to you. See, we're all on our way to meet the Wizard to get Jack here—

JACK: Howdy!

DOROTHY: A brain, and Tinker the Tin Man—

TINKER: Hello!

DOROTHY: A heart. Maybe if the Wizard is powerful enough, he could give you some courage as well?

EUGENE: Jumpin' Jackrabbits! You really think so? Why, that'd be stupendous! That'd be extraordinary! Imagine it, me, not afraid of nothing or nobody! Boy, would my parents be proud!

JACK: So does that mean you'll come with us then?

EUGENE: Why I'd love to come! In fact, I will come! And when all this is said and done, I'll be the bravest, most masculine lion there is! There's only one thing I need to do first!

TINKER: And what's that?

EUGENE: Why grab my baby blue blanky for the road, of course. I never leave home without it. *(To the blanket—as if speaking to a baby or small dog:)* No, I don't, no I don't, no, no, no, no.

(He and blanket embrace. Toto growls.)

JACK: Believe me, Toto; whatever you're saying, we're all thinking the same thing.

(The group begins to walk in place as Nigel narrates.)

NIGEL: "And so, once more the little company set off upon their journey. Eugene, walking with timid strides, at Dorothy's side. Toto did not approve of this new comrade at first, but after a time he became more at ease, and presently Toto and the Cowardly Lion had grown to be good friends."

EUGENE: *(To Toto:)* Come here, you!

SCENE 2: THE POPPY FIELD
CHOOSE YOUR OWN DANCE

NIGEL: "As they continued to walk, they listened intently to what they thought was the singing of some brightly colored birds.

(Harmonizing can be heard off in the distance.)

But the closer and closer they came to the source of their ears' entertainment, the sooner they realized that the harmonious notes hadn't been coming from the birds at all — "

DOROTHY/EUGENE/TINKER/JACK: They hadn't?

NIGEL: They hadn't — "but instead from the lovely flowers which now became so thick that the ground was carpeted with them."

(The POPPIES enter.)

"They were big yellow and white and blue and purple clusters of Poppies, which were so brilliant in color they almost dazzled Dorothy's eyes."

DOROTHY: Everyone look! Aren't they beautiful?

EUGENE: I think so!

TINKER: I know so!

JACK: Eh, I guess so.

POPPIES: *(Crossing their stems in disapproval:)* Hmph!

JACK: What I mean is, when I have some brains I'll probably like them — and appreciate them — better.

DOROTHY: *(To the Poppies:)* Well Toto and I think you're beautiful, don't we Toto? Toto? Toto?

TINKER: Um...Dorothy.

(Tinker points to Toto who, cow or dog, is lifting his leg and is about to do something rather naughty on the Poppies! The Poppies squeal in terror!)

DOROTHY: Toto, no! Down boy! Heel!

(Toto does as he's told and regretfully approaches his owner.)

I'm sorry about that. Toto sometimes just can't contain his excitement.

EUGENE: That makes two of us.

(The sound of a toilet flushing can be heard as Eugene walks out from behind a bush, wiping his brow with his blanket.)

DOROTHY: Now that we've completed the "Embarrass Dorothy" portion of our trip, I say it's time to get a move on! Hmmm, it looks as if the Yellow Brick Road goes through this field of flowers, so I'm guessing we should too. *(To Poppies:)* Would that be all right with you?

(The Poppies merrily part, providing the group a path to walk through.)

Thank you, thank you very much. Come on, guys!

EUGENE: I dunno, Dorothy. Do you think it's safe?

TINKER: C'mon Eugene, they're just harmless flowers.

JACK: Nothin' to worry about at all.

(The Poppies snicker gleefully.)

Right?

POPPIES: *(Crossing their fingers...err...stems:)* Mmhmm.

JACK: See.

EUGENE: Okay...if you say so. C'mon, blanky.

(Dorothy and the group begin to walk in place, as they trek through the Poppy Field. As they do this, the Poppies harmonize and hum a lullaby.)

DOROTHY: See, this isn't so bad. Everything out here is so peaceful...

JACK: And quiet too!

DOROTHY: Agreed. In fact, all this piece and quiet is...is... *(With a large yawn:)* Kind of exhausting.

EUGENE: You know, I gotta agree with you.

JACK: Me too...

NIGEL: And me three... HUH?! WHAT? Was I falling asleep again? No, no, no, this won't do. In case you haven't figured it out yet, the poppy fields are really evil...

(The Poppies laugh maniacally.)

And use their powers to make our heroes...

(CRASH! Toto falls over on his back in exhaustion, his four paws sticking up out of the grass.)

Pass out. Boring, right? And exhausting! But I think I know how we can change things up! Don't you?

(He blows his whistle, which wakes all the characters up with a start.)

PAUSE!

EUGENE: *(Hiding behind Dorothy:)* Wha—what was that?!

NIGEL: That, Eugene, was my handy little whistle and THIS...

(He snaps his fingers as a giant, Wheel of Fortune-esque spinning wheel is rolled onstage. Perhaps music accompanies.)

Is the SPIN-O-RAMA 3000!

GROUP: Spin-O-Rama 3000?

NIGEL: That's right! These guys and I don't want to sit here and watch you guys sleep all day.

POPPIES: Aww!

NIGEL: Sorry, Poppies. But since these flowers like music and we, the audience, like music as well, we thought that, instead of sleeping, you five could dance! On the SPIN-O-RAMA 3000 we have all sorts of dances you guys can do—all we need now is a volunteer to help us figure out what moves you guys will be performing.

(Nigel selects a volunteer and escorts him/her over to the SPIN-O-RAMA.)

(A few notes about this wheel: you can put as many or as few dance moves on it as you like, just as long as the actors are familiar with all of them. A few that I suggest are ones that are similar to Michael Jackson's "Thriller," "The Macarena," "The Robot," or anything else that requires large, exaggerated movements and repetitive steps.)

(The scene should play out something like this: once Nigel selects a volunteer, he explains that all he/she need do is give the wheel two or three good spins, and whatever dance the spinner lands on, that's the one Dorothy and her crew will be required to perform. While the wheel is spinning, perhaps game show music plays in the background. Once the dance is selected, Nigel encourages the audience to applaud for the volunteer and helps him/her down off the stage. The following plays out as such.)

(Clearing his throat:) Time to continue! "And so, as the Poppy flowers sang their intoxicating tune, Dorothy, the Lion, the Tin Man, the Scarecrow, and Toto, were helpless to do nothing but shake their money makers and dance to the music!"

(Music underscores as the group does just that.)

DOROTHY: This is awful! I don't know what to do!

TINKER/JACK/EUGENE: I know!

DOROTHY: We could be trapped dancing here forever!

TINKER/JACK/EUGENE: I know!

DOROTHY: And dancing in heels is anything but comfortable!

TINKER/JACK/EUGENE: I know!

JACK: ...Wait.

(The Poppies, ignoring this conversation, continue to harmonize and high five each other with delight. The group continues their dance)

TINKER: Oh, my head is sweating and feet are rusting from all this movement! If only there were someone out there who could help us! But alas, we might as well kiss our patooties goodbye!

DOROTHY: *Kiss?* Kiss! That's it, Tinker! *(Rubbing her forehead:)* Kiss!

TINKER: Dorothy as attractive as I find you, I don't think romance is the answer right now!

DOROTHY: No, Tin Man! Glinda she gave me a... *(To audience:)* Remember, you guys, when Glinda gave me her kiss? What do you think, should I ask her for help? Now's as good a time as any, right? *(Waits for response.)* Me too! Glinda! Oh, Glinda!

NIGEL: "And then, as if by magic, at the uttering of her name... Poof!..."

GLINDA: *(POOF!)* I'm here! DIVA POSE!

NIGEL: "Glinda returned!"

DOROTHY: Oh Glinda, are we ever glad to see you!

JACK: We're in great big trouble!

TOTO: Bark! Bark!

GLINDA: Yes, I can see that. You call that dancing? Back in my day this is how we used to do it! Hit it, boys!

(She snaps her fingers causing the music to screech to a halt and change. She does a step or two, kicking up her heels and singing to herself. She stops and poses, waiting for applause.)

GROUP: GLINDA!

(The music picks back up as it was before, causing Dorothy and the group to continue their dance.)

GLINDA: Kidding! Kidding! Don't worry, my babies. With a simple wave of my jewel-encrusted wand the music will stop and the dancing will...

(She flicks her wand. Beat. Nothing happens.)

EUGENE: *(Panicking:)* The dancing will what? The dancing will what?

GLINDA: Huh. That's never happened before. *(Waving her wand, perhaps breathing on it:)* Testing...testing...one, two, three... *(It lights up!)* Ah! There we go! And now, the music will stop and the dancing will...CEASE!

(The music stops! The group is finally able to stop dancing.)

(To the Poppies:) Now begone, you! Go!

(The Poppies angrily exit.)

JACK: We're free!

EUGENE: Thank the heavens!

JACK: Thank the lord!

DOROTHY: Thank—

GLINDA: *(Through chuckles and giggles:)* Glinda!

DOROTHY: Oh yes! Thank you, Glinda!

TINKER: Yes, for everything! Why, I'm so happy I could cry!

DOROTHY/EUGENE/JACK: Don't!

GLINDA: Please, please, think EVERYthing of it! Now if that'll be all, I'll just collect my kiss...

> *(She touches Dorothy's forehead, makes a silly sound, and steps away.)*

And be on my fabulous way. One thing though, Dorothy: unfortunately, this was the only service I'm permitted to provide you with, so make sure you and your...whatever these three are...quicken your pace and head straight for the Wizard's Emerald Palace. Word on the street is that Mumbi has sent something after you, and from what I hear, *(Aside to Nigel:)* it ain't pretty.

NIGEL: Tell me about it.

GLINDA: Now I'm off! I have goodness to spread and not a lot of time to do it in! Goodbye all! Goodbye Dorothy, *(Petting Toto:)* Goodbye Tarantino! *(In an operatic tone:)* Cheerio, loves! DIVA OUT!

> *(POOF! Glinda exits.)*

NIGEL: "And with that, she was gone. Dorothy and her friends took Glinda's advice and shuffled along, stopping only when necessary..."

> *(Lights fade on the group as Nigel continues to talk.)*

SCENE 3: OUTSIDE THE GATES
OF THE EMERALD CITY

NIGEL: "Finally, just when their journey seemed like it would never end, they saw a beautiful green glow in the sky reflecting off the mountain tops. As they walked on, the glow became brighter, and brighter, and brighter, and just when they thought they couldn't stand it anymore..."

JACK: Look! We made it! The Emerald Palace is straight up ahead!

TINKER: Oh boy! Oh joy!

DOROTHY: *(Running in place:)* Just a little further and we're there! Wizard of Oz, here we come! And to think, we were worried about the Witch of the West.

JACK: Worried! Ha! What's there to worry about when we're so close? I don't need a brain to realize that there's nothing she can do now!

TINKER: No, sir! We're as good as there! In fact, I think I can feel my heart beating already!

EUGENE: And I my courage! Oh, you guys are right, that ol' Witch was nothin' to fear at all! In fact, I wish she was here right now! I'd give her a piece of mind! Oh, you bet I would!

MUMBI: *(Voiceover:)* Is that so, Lion? Well, fortunately for you, I'm all ears!

(POOF! She appears, a cloud of smoke surrounding her. She hacks her lungs out.)

Seriously?! Is it just me or are these entrances getting smokier and smokier?! Jeez, Stagehand Number 1 *[or whatever crew member you'd like to call out that day]*, tone it down will you? We get it! We get it! Now, where were we? Oh yes, you may commence with the panicking.

EUGENE: Cool. *(Through high pitched screams:)* Ahhhh! It—it—it's the witch!

MUMBI: That's right, kitty cat! But don't worry, I didn't come alone! Oh boys...

(Mumbi snaps her fingers as an army of Flying Monkeys...or Pigs, or Pokeys, whichever the audience selected, steps forth. Obviously change the lines accordingly.)

DOROTHY: What are *those*?

MUMBI: Nothing really, just my personal army of bloodthirsty, flesh-eating, magical flying monkeys!

GROUP: Ahhh!

(If the audience has selected the Ponkeys, the following dialogue should follow after: Blood-thirsty, flesh-eating, magical flying Ponkeys!)

*PONKEY SCENARIO

TINKER: Wait...Ponkeys?

DOROTHY: Wha — wha — what's a Ponkey?

MUMBI: You know, Ponkeys. Half pig, half monkey! Ponkey.

GROUP: Ahhh.

MUMBI: My babies, these are the nitwits I was telling you about! It's time to put a stop to them once and for all! As your master, I order you to attack! ATTACK! ATTACK!!!!

(Mumbi's minions begin chasing Dorothy and Toto, while Jack and Tinker try and ward them off. All the while Eugene, searching for a hiding place, throws his blanket over his head and stands perfectly still. Music underscores.)

(A few notes about the chase sequence: it is to be highly theatrical, and should hopefully involve Dorothy, Toto, and the Monkeys running through the audience. Perhaps Dorothy and Toto beg the audience to help hide them. While all this is going on, Nigel, Tinker, Jack, Eugene, and Mumbi shout out orders to the Monkeys like, "Leave them alone!" or, for Mumbi, "Catch them, you fools!" The goal is to get the audience as involved as possible.)

(Eventually, the Monkeys snatch up Dorothy and Toto, and exit through the audience. As the last Monkey is about to leave, Eugene begins whipping him with his blue blanket.)

EUGENE: You—you—rude, Monkey thing!

(The Monkey, in frustration, lunges at Eugene, ripping the blanket out of his hands and shredding it to pieces.)

Not my blanky! Not—not my BLANKY!! Why? *Oh WHY?!?*

(Eugene melts into a puddle of tears.)

NIGEL: "The witch chortled in her joy as she made plans to return back to her palace."

MUMBI: *(Checking off her checklist:)* Nice work, boys! Capture the girl? Check! Capture her dog? Check. Laugh maniacally? *(She does so.)* Double check. A most productive day!

NIGEL: "But she had forgotten about one thing!"

JACK: Wait, where are you taking Dorothy?

MUMBI: Ugh, you three. What am I going to do with you? I suppose I should destroy you...but all this evil-doing has exhausted me, and there's still have plenty left to do when I get home. What to do? I've got it, I'll let you live, *for now*, but don't even THINK about trying to save your friend, because if you do, I'll make sure you regret what's left of your miserable little lives! Understand? *(She cackles again!)* So long losers! See you on the upside of never!

(Mumbi exits, leaving Tinker, Jack, and Eugene alone onstage.)

EUGENE: Oh, please bring Dorothy back! Please! Please! Ppplllleeeaaasssee! *(Beat.)* Call me crazy, but I don't think they're bringing her back.

TINKER: *(Through sniffles:)* I think you're right, Eugene. What are we gonna do now?

JACK: I'll tell yah what we're NOT gonna do! We're not gonna cry, and we're not gonna hide behind our tails neither!

EUGENE: *(From under his ripped blanket:)* What about blankets — can we hide behind them?

JACK: No, we can't — not if we want to rescue Dorothy that is!

TINKER/EUGENE: Rescue Dorothy?

TINKER: But didn't you hear what the witch said?

JACK: I did not, I was too busy coming up with a plan, and I think it's a good one! First, you Tinker should —

EUGENE: *(Clutching the blanket:)* Look, Jack, plan or no plan, there's no way I'm messing with Mumbi. Not after what she did to my baby.

TINKER: Not after what she did to us! It's too dangerous!

EUGENE: And scary!

JACK: C'mon you two, we just can't abandon Dorothy like this. Think of all she's done for you. If it weren't for her, why Tinker you'd still be wandering aimlessly in those woods...

TINKER: That is true...

JACK: And lion, you'd still be cowering behind that bush.

EUGENE: Touché...

JACK: And, as for me, why I'd still be sitting by my lonesome in a cornfield somewhere, waiting for a miracle to occur. Fortunately though, a miracle DID occur, and I don't know about the rest of you, but I'll be darned if I'm gonna let some witch take her away without a fight! What do ya say... *(Putting out his hand:)* For Dorothy?

EUGENE/JACK/TINKER: *(Putting their hands/paws in as well:)* FOR DOROTHY!

NIGEL: For Dorothy! *(Beat.)* ...Sorry. Got caught up in the moment.

EUGENE: And for Toto, too!

JACK: All right, here's how it's going to go down; I'll whisper the plan inaudibly into your ears while Nigel here narrates! You guys with me?

TINKER: You bet we are!

EUGENE: A hundred percent, and then some!

JACK: Great! Take it away, Mister Narrator!

NIGEL: With pleasure, Jack!

(Nigel begins to read as Jack whispers his scheme into Eugene and Tinker's ears.)

"And so, Jack relayed his plan to Eugene and Tinker, hoping beyond hope that it was clever enough to outwit Mumbi and rescue Dorothy. Speaking of Dorothy..."

SCENE 4: MUMBI'S TORTURE CHAMBER
CHOOSE THE WITCH'S COMEUPPANCE

(The scene shifts to Mumbi's torture chamber. Dorothy is bound and gagged to a chair.)

NIGEL: "She now found herself in the most terrible of places; the torture chamber of the Witched Witch of the West! And Mumbi, of course, was tormenting our heroine with the most horrible affliction known to man!"

MUMBI: That's right, and now it's time for you...to look at my scrapbook!

(Mumbi sits next to Dorothy, a scrapbook open in front of her.)

Let's see... Oh! Here's me in front of the world's largest ball of yarn,

(Dorothy begs and pleads under her gag.)

and look, here's one of me at a Zipper Museum—it's always open, don't ya know.

(Dorothy moans a muffled moan.)

Ah! And here's me at a pencil sharpening factory, which I assure you, is anything but POINTLESS. Ha-ha!

DOROTHY: *(Moaning and groaning, she spits out her gag:)* No more! Please! No more!

MUMBI: Had enough already, have you? And I didn't even have to pull out my slides from Hawaii. You're weaker than I anticipated. Which is all the better for me! Now give me those shoes of yours and you can go free!

DOROTHY: But we tried that already. They're stuck tight! I can't!

MUMBI: Can't or *won't?* We'll see if you change your tune once I bring in your... *(She claps her hands.)* Mangy Little Mutt! *(If Toto is a cow:)* Sordid Little Sow! *(Beat. Nothing happens. Mumbi clears her throat. She clears it again.)* I said, "Bring in your Mangy Little Mutt!" Hello? Is anyone listening back there? *(Mumbling to herself as she exits:)* Ugh. You want something done right, you've got to do it yourself. *(Off:)* Monkey, what are you doing?

(The Monkey squeaks, or if it's a Pig, oinks, or if it's a Ponkey, squeaks and oinks, its answers. As he and Mumbi ad-lib back and forth, Dorothy begins to untie her hands.)

I don't care if you're on a coffee break! I'm trying to be evil and threatening here and you're ruining it for me.

NIGEL: *(Whispering rhythmically:)* Psst...good job! Go Dorothy, go! Go Dorothy, go! *(To audience:)* Come on everybody, let's cheer her on! Go Dorothy, Go! Go Dorothy, Go! Go Dorothy,

Go!

(Finally, Dorothy unties herself as Nigel encourages the audience to applaud.)

MUMBI: And what's going on out here?!

(As Mumbi enters again, Dorothy throws her untied hands behind her back to avoid suspicion.)

Narrator?

NIGEL: Nothing, Mumbi. *(To audience:)* Right guys? *(Waits for response:)* See?

MUMBI: You'd better be telling the truth, Narrator—or else I'll fix you next. Now, as I was saying, Dorothy; if you don't give me those shoes, then unfortunately I'll be forced to hurt your DOG!

(Monkey enters with a chained up Toto.)

DOROTHY: *(Gasping:)* Toto! Oh, Toto!

MUMBI: *(Mimicking her:)* Yes, Toto! Now what's it going to be, girl? Well...

(Dorothy looks back and forth, from her shoes to dog, unsure of what to do.)

NIGEL: "And then, just as Dorothy was about to lose all hope"—along with your Narrator—

(Mumbi laughs maniacally. Suddenly the doorbell rings a jaunty little ring.)

MUMBI: NOW WHAT?! Ain't it always the way—you're in the midst of a really wicked laugh and the doorbell rings? Well...don't just wait around...answer the door!

(The Monkey does as he's told. Jack, wearing a top hat and mustache, enters with a large cart being pushed by Eugene and Tinker, who are also sporting hats and mustaches.)

Who is it?

JACK: It is I, ah...Martin...uh...Merlham, Monster Merchant extraordinaire!

MUMBI: Monster merchant?

JACK: *(Wooing her:)* That's right! I was told that you, Madame Mumbi, are not only the wickedest witch the West has ever seen, but also the one and only Queen of Mean.

MUMBI: Oh Merchant, go on. I SAID, GO ON!

JACK: Yes! I was also told that you're always in the monster market, constantly looking for the newest, nastiest monster around to do your dastardly bidding, AND I was told that good help is hard to find.

(Mumbi and Jack look over at the Monkey who is happily picking his nose.)

MUMBI: Boy is that true. *(To Monkey:)* Shoo, Monkey! Don't bother me!

(Monkey exits.)

JACK: Fortunately, you are in luck, as the answer to all your problems is in this very cart. You see, I have captured a beast like no other! He's got ten eyes, twelve toes...ah...four fingernails, and two hundred and twenty-seven...uh...noses!

MUMBI: Noses?

JACK: Yes, noses! And if that doesn't sound terrifying enough, wait til you hear his roar! *(Tapping against the box:)* Go ahead beast, roar.

EUGENE: Uh...roar.

JACK: See.

MUMBI: You call that a roar? Why it sounds...positively putrid! I must see this creature now!

JACK: All right, if you're sure... Guards, open the door.

(Eugene and Tinker open the door.)

MUMBI: Outta my way, nitwits! New monster, meet your new master!

(Mumbi rushes in.)

DOROTHY: Psst...Martin Merlhan, or whoever you are, please don't sell her another monster to torture me with!

JACK: It's gonna be all right, Dorothy.

DOROTHY: Wait, how'd you know my—

MUMBI: *(From inside the cart:)* Wait a second! There isn't a monster in this cart.

TINKER: That's where you're wrong, Mumbi.

EUGENE: Mmmhmm. See, there wasn't before—

JACK: BUT THERE IS NOW! Shut it, guys!

(SLAM! Tinker, Jack, and Eugene slam the door shut!)

MUMBI: What's the meaning of this! You let me out this instant! You hear me? Let me out!

EUGENE: Quiet, you! Or I'll roar again, ha-ha! Roar!

DOROTHY: Thank you so much for rescuing me!

(She begins untying Toto.)

TOTO: *(Muffled from the gag:)* Bark-Bark.

DOROTHY: You three have helped me ever so much, and yet I don't even know who you are.

TINKER: You mean you haven't guessed?

EUGENE: You mean you can't tell?

DOROTHY: No.

(Toto shakes his head and gives a muffled dog-like "no.")

MUMBI: Not a clue.

JACK: Wow, and people say I'm the one in need of brains.

NIGEL: "Dorothy could not believe her eyes, for one moment three strangers stood before her, and the next..."

DOROTHY: Lion, and Scarecrow, and Tin Man! Oh my!

NIGEL: "Three close friends!"

DOROTHY: I'm so happy you're here! I never thought I'd see you again!

TINKER: *(Through tears:)* And we never thought we'd see you.

DOROTHY: I just can't believe you risked everything...to help me. Weren't you frightened?

EUGENE: Talkin' tadpoles, you bet we were! But even then we—

TINKER: Were just so worried about you that—

JACK: That nothing else seemed to matter.

DOROTHY: *(Touched:)* You guys! You're the best middle-aged, adult, single male friends a young girl could ask for! Group hug!

DOROTHY/NIGEL/TINKER/EUGENE/JACK/TOTO: Awwww.

MUMBI: How touching! You all should be so proud—for now! It was foolish of me not to finish you three stooges off when I had the chance! Luckily though, I'll have another chance once I get out of here!

TINKER: She's right! That crate isn't gonna hold her forever!

EUGENE: Whatta we do? Whatta we do?

DOROTHY: Um...huddle up!

(The group huddles together, ad-libbing loudly and inaudibly what their next plan of action should be. As they do this, two things occur — one, Mumbi loudly attempts to escape from the cart, ramming her body against the door. This clearly does not work. Two, a MAID enters, a large bucket of water in her hands. She whistles as she walks. She puts the bucket down and begins scrubbing the floors. To the group:)

This isn't helping at all.

JACK: I know, it's so hard to think with all that banging —

EUGENE: Yeah, and with that maid's whistling and scrubbing. If only she'd take her large bucket of water — AKA the one and only substance on this planet that can stop a witch — and go somewhere else!

DOROTHY/TINKER/JACK: Wait — WHAT?!?!

DOROTHY: That's it! Water!

(The group races over to the Maid, who screams and exits when she sees them coming. They each take an end and approach the cart as Eugene mans the door's lever.)

TINKER: *(Encouraging the children in the audience to participate:)* On the count of three! One — Two —

(Eugene pulls the lever that opens the doors and Mumbi, a bit disoriented from throwing herself against the door, emerges.)

MUMBI: I'm free! I'm free! And now, shoes or no shoes, I'm going to destroy you, *Dorothy*, and for good this time! For after all, I am darkness, I am evil, I AM —

DOROTHY: Three!

(SPLASH!!! The water lands on Mumbi.)

MUMBI: *(Spitting out the water:)* ...Gonna melt now! *(Throwing herself on the ground and comically thrashing about:)* No, not me! I'm too young and evil to die this way! No! No! Somebody!

HELP!!!

(This goes on for several beats.)

NIGEL: *(After blowing his whistle:)* PAUSE!

DOROTHY/JACK/TINKER/EUGENE/TOTO: What!?

NIGEL: Pause.

MUMBI: Okay, even I'll say it—WHAT?!

DOROTHY: Narrator, what are you doing?

EUGENE: Yeah, we were just about to vanquish the Wicked Witch!

NIGEL: I know that, Lion, but as I was looking over the text here I realized melting someone isn't the answer—just like violence is never the answer.

TINKER: Very true.

NIGEL: Besides, by just doing away with Mumbi, by sending her off into oblivion, she'll never really pay for all the damage she's done, or think about all the harm she's brought to others.

JACK: That is true.

MUMBI: But, but I don't want to *think*. How awful would that be? Besides, if I were to "think" about it, I think I'd think this new punishment almost sounds worse.

NIGEL: Trust me, it is. But, of course, this is just my opinion and not the audience's. So I think we all should take it to a vote. *(To audience:)* What do you say, guys? How many of you want to just melt the witch?

(Mumbi encourages them to vote for this choice while Dorothy and the group encourage them to do the opposite.)

And how many of you think she should really be punished? She should stew on what she's done and be forced to pay for her actions?

(Mumbi now encourages the kids to not vote for this second choice while Dorothy and the group do everything in their power to make the audience select option number two.)

(Playwright's note: Unlike the other "choose-your-own" elements in the show, this one is nonnegotiable. I think it's important to keep this show as light as possible and teach the audience that violence is never the answer.)

And it looks like Mumbi is NOT going to melt after all!

MUMBI: But, but Narrator—you can't do this to me! It's wrong, it's—it's bad manners.

NIGEL: Well, fortunately for you, *those are the only kind of manners you like.* So "while the water did not melt the witch as originally intended, it instead stripped her of her powers, making her a servant to the Flying Monkeys and their monkey-like demands—"

MUMBI: What?

(The Monkeys enter and begin pulling Mumbi offstage.)

NIGEL: "Some of which included cleaning up after them, tucking them in at night, and of course grooming their matted and messy, bug-filled hair!"

(A Monkey approaches Mumbi and wants her to "groom" him.)

MUMBI: I'm not going to do this! Someone, help me! Dorothy!? Scarecrow? Tin Man-I-Created-Then-Abandoned? Lion? What about you, Lion? Will you help me?

EUGENE: Help you? Witch, please. You hurt my friends, misused your powers, and worst of all...ripped my blanky. Take her away, Monkeys! Roar!

MUMBI: Noooo!

(The Monkeys and Mumbi exit.)

NIGEL: "And with that, the witch was vanquished!!

(Dorothy and the group cheer, celebrate, and high five. Perhaps they even high five some of the kids in the audience.)

"Finally, Dorothy and her companions were able to travel in peace, and once they left Mumbi's lair, made it quickly and safely to the Wizard's palace."

DOROTHY: *(To Nigel:)* You mean it? After all this, we're finally going to meet the Wizard?

NIGEL: Indeed, you are.

(Trumpets sound as the lights shift. A beautiful palace is seen in the background.)

GROUP: *Oooh! Ahhh. Preeetttyyy.*

NIGEL: "Now, because the Wizard's palace was made of bright, shining emeralds, the companions were told to wear green glasses...

(They all put on green spectacles.)

...to shield their eyes from the glare. And so, hand, in hand, in hand, in paw, they locked arms and made their way to a great throne room of the great and powerful Oz!

SCENE 5: THE WIZARD'S THRONE ROOM
CHOOSE YOUR OWN ENDING

(Darkness. Silence. A knocking is heard, followed by more silence. A creaking door opens as Dorothy pokes her head in.)

DOROTHY: Um... excuse me... Mister Oz... Mister Great... Mister Powerful... Oz?

EUGENE: *(Poking his head in:)* Ma—maybe he's not here,

maybe we should go back home?

TINKER: Nonsense, we have to go in, what other choice do we have?

JACK: I agree! Well...here goes nothing.

(They all enter the dark room. A spot rests on them.)

DOROTHY: Oh Mister Wizard...

JACK: *(Whistling:)* Here boy, here.

TOTO: Bark-bark.

TINKER: Where are you, Mister Wizard?

EUGENE: Yeah, where are you Mister —

(The lights flicker as a booming voice comes from stage left. It is the WIZARD OF OZ himself!)

OZ: OZ!!!! I AM OZ, THE GREAT AND TERRIBLE!!! WHO ARE YOU, AND WHY DO YOU SEEK ME?!

(Eugene trembles in his place.)

I SAID, WHY DO YOU SEEK ME?!

EUGENE: I gotta get outta here, I gotta get —

DOROTHY: No, Lion, not now! It'd be senseless to turn back now!

EUGENE: And yet, being senseless seems so sensible.

OZ: WELL? I'M WAITING FOR AN ANSWER!! WHO ARE YOU? WHO! ARE! YOU!?!

DOROTHY: If—if you please, your greatness, I am Dorothy Gale, the small and meek. I've come a long way to ask you to send me back to Kansas.

OZ: KANSAS?! WHY WOULD ANYONE WANT TO GO THERE?

DOROTHY: Because it's my home, sir.

OZ: I SEE. AND TELL ME, WHO IS THIS YOU'VE BROUGHT WITH YOU?

JACK: I'm Jack, the scarecrow, your Ozness...ness, and these are my friends. Tinker—

TINKER: Hello there sir...wizard...uh...sir wizard.

JACK: And this is Eugene the Cowardly Lion. Go ahead, Eugene, say hello.

EUGENE: *(In a high pitched, squeaky voice:)* ...Hello...

JACK: We've come to ask you for a brain, a heart, and some courage!

OZ: IS THAT SO?!

TINKER: Yes your, your wizardship! That is, if it's not too much trouble...for you.

OZ: AS A MATTER OF FACT, SCARECROW, IT IS! I'M SURE YOU'RE WELL AWARE THE GREAT OZ IS VERY BUSY THESE DAYS AND CAN'T JUST GO ABOUT SOLVING EVERYONE'S PROBLEMS. WHY, IF THAT WERE THE CASE THEN PEOPLE WOULD CONSTANTLY BE SHOWING UP AT MY DOOR AND I WOULDN'T HAVE TIME TO DO THE THINGS THAT...WELL...WIZARDS NORMALLY DO! THAT SAID, COME BACK TOMORROW AND I WILL DECIDE WHETHER OR NOT I WILL GRANT YOUR REQUEST!

GROUP: TOMORROW?!

OZ: IS THERE AN ECHO IN HERE...HERE...HERE...HERE...

EUGENE: Actually, there is—

OZ: I SAID, TOMORROW!

JACK: But—but we came all this way!

TINKER: Yeah! And we even vanquished the Wicked Witch of the West—

DOROTHY: And stripped her of her powers!

OZ: REALLY NOW? TELL ME...LION...IS THIS TRUE?

EUGENE: I—I—

OZ: WELL?! I'M WAITING FOR AN ANSWER! IS IT TRUE!?!!

EUGENE: I—I—Ahhhhhh!!!

DOROTHY: *(To the Wizard:)* Now look what you've done!

(Eugene, panicking, begins running around in circles, perhaps screaming "GET ME OUTTA HERE, GET ME OUTTA HERE!" or something like that. Dorothy, Jack, and Tinker, try and calm him down, telling him it'll be all right while the Wizard booms, "STOP THIS! STOP IT AT ONCE!" All of their attempts are in vain.)

EUGENE: *(Spying a little green curtain—spoken over his comrades' cries:)* I've gotta hide! I've gotta hide! But where?!

(The following lines are spoken over one another.)

DOROTHY: Eugene, come back!

JACK: Don't hide!

TINKER: Come back! Come back!

OZ: WHAT ARE YOU DOING? WHAT IS HE DOING?! DON'T GO BEHIND THAT CURTAIN! YOU HEAR ME?!?! I SAID DON'T GO BEHIND—

(Suddenly, Eugene rips the curtain open and sees a man, Nigel in a top hat and fake mustache, manning what looks to be a tiny control room. The group gasps.)

NIGEL: ...That curtain.

DOROTHY: What—what's going on here?

JACK: Yeah! Who are you?

NIGEL: Isn't it obvious, kids? I'm...the Wonderful Wizard...of Oz. Ta dah.

GROUP: What?!

JACK: That's not true!

TINKER: You can't be him!

EUGENE: You're just pullin' our tails.

DOROTHY: Guys, wait; I think he's telling the truth. He is the wizard. Glinda told me I'd know him when I see him...and... *(To Nigel:)* It's really you? Isn't it?

NIGEL: It is. I am...the Wizard *(Aside, to the audience, lowering his mustache:)* At least for this scene.

DOROTHY: But I don't understand. There was all this smoke and...and your voice, it was so loud and booming! What happened?

NIGEL: Just a few of my many tricks. I'm really a magician, see. A conjurer, a trickster, a —

JACK: Phony?

NIGEL: Yes...that too.

DOROTHY: This is terrible, and to think we went through all this...for nothing. Oh, now you'll never get your heart, Tinker, or your courage, Eugene, or your brain, Jack. This whole trip was a waste.

NIGEL: Wait a minute, wait just a cotton pickin' minute. You mean to tell me you three were actually serious you when asked me to give you those things?

JACK: Of course we were!

EUGENE: *(Under his blanket:)* Don't we look serious?

NIGEL: Indeed you do, and you know what else you look like? Heroes! Heroes that already possess the very parts that they're asking for.

TINKER: Wait! We do?

EUGENE: Huh?

JACK: Is this another one of your tricks?

NIGEL: I assure you, Jack, it's anything but. Think about it—if you didn't already possess a brain, a heart, and a heaping helping of courage, how could you possibly defeat Mumbi, let alone make it to my throne room?

EUGENE: Dancing Dolphins! He's right!

JACK: You know, I guess he is. And I guess it turns out we had what we wanted all along! Huh, when you really think about it, this whole ordeal was kind of silly.

TINKER: I don't think so. If we'd known earlier, if we hadn't wanted a brain, or a heart, or courage so badly, then we never would've met Dorothy and—wait, Dorothy! What about her?

EUGENE: Yeah, are ya able to help her too?

NIGEL: Hmmm...that depends. See Dorothy, as you've probably already guessed, I don't possess any real magical powers, but I think I can aid you in your journey home.

DOROTHY: You mean it? Really?

NIGEL: I do, but I must ask you first...what do *you* consider to be a home? What does that word mean to you?

DOROTHY: Well, a home is some place where you're happy, where you're surrounded by loved ones, and friends and...and people who are willing to stick their necks out for you, and stand by your side, even when things are tough.

NIGEL: And wouldn't you say that's exactly what these fine fellows did this afternoon when they rescued you?

DOROTHY: You know, you're right. They did do that for me, and more! Gee, I've been so concerned about going back to my home in Kansas, that I failed to realize I created a home for myself right here in Oz with you three!

TOTO: Uh... Bark.

DOROTHY: And of course, you too, Toto!

NIGEL: I guess now it's decision time for you, Dorothy. If you really want to go back to Kansas, then all you need to do is click those enchanted heels of yours together three times, and command them to carry you wherever you wish to go. BUT if you choose to stay here, and that's a permanent choice mind you, I think I know three fellows who'd be more than happy to have you.

JACK/TINKER/EUGENE: You bet!/That's right/Ain't it the truth!

DOROTHY: And I love you all dearly, but, I also love my Uncle and Aunt. Heavens, Mister Wizard, what should I do? I'm happy in both places. Which one should I choose?

NIGEL: Now that is the question, isn't it? But I think I have an idea. *(To audience:)* Since today's show is all about YOU and YOUR choices, I think it's best we allow YOU, our friends, and our dear, dear audience, to decided individually where you'd like to see Dorothy end up!

(The group shakes their head in agreement.)

TINKER: That's a great idea!

JACK: Indubitably!

DOROTHY: I'll say! And to think, this whole time I've not wanted my story to change, and yet by doing so this time, it's as if I get the best of both worlds.

NIGEL: Here's hoping. Now to do this properly, I want everybody, all of you, to close your eyes, close 'em real tight— you too, Lion—and imagine the place you think Dorothy would be happiest—and then poof, through the magic of your imagination, that's where she'll be, and that's where she'll live.

JACK: I'm picking Oz.

TINKER: I'm picking Kansas.

EUGENE: And I'm choosing Vegas!

DOROTHY: I love this, Nigel! Thank you!!

NIGEL: You're welcome! The only sad part now Dorothy is that it is here where we bid you, and everyone else, adieu for the evening,

EUGENE: Aww, and say our goodbyes?

TINKER: Yes. But before we go, we do want to thank you for not only participating in our story,

JACK: But for helping us tell it in a way that we never could have without you.

EUGENE: Nope.

DOROTHY: And so, as we look out at all your bright, shining faces, wishing you the safest of travels, and warmest of car rides, we want to remind you that wherever you're headed, whatever your final destination may be tonight, in the end, there really is...

COMPANY: No. Place. Like. Home.

TOTO: Bark! Bark!

> (*Dorothy clicks her heels together three times. Trumpets blare. Lights out. Silence.*)

The Author Speaks

What inspired you to write this play?

I was asked to write a *Wizard of Oz* adaptation for Louisiana's historic Cassidy Park in 2013, and while I was delighted at the notion of working with such a beloved story, I wanted to make sure that my adaptation stood out from the millions of others. While expressing this to a former professor of mine, it became clear, to the both of us that a participation-heavy re-telling of *Oz* was not only the way to go, but the way to make certain elements of the story that can seem stale and routine, fresh and exciting again. I soon came up with the Choose Your Own approach, and after doing a bit of research, voila, the play was practically writing itself.

Was the structure or other elements of the play influenced by any other work?

I've used audience participation before, primarily in my works *The Big Bad Bullysaurus* and *Charlie the No-Good, Really-Rotten Cheat-A-Saurus Rex,* and those moments really shaped the structure of this piece. I also did my homework and read and re-read a few Choose Your Own Adventures to see how that style of storytelling would work in a theatrical piece. I did my best to break the play's scenes up into "chapters," as a way to give the piece as a whole a real literary feel. If I've done my job right, the play will feel as if it truly is a storybook come to life.

Have you dealt with the same theme in other works that you have written?

I've used audience participation before, but never to this extent. When it comes to writing for children, especially children's theatre, I think it is important to allow your young audience to take part in the story that's unfolding before them. Kids have so many wonderful ideas and curious thoughts, and as actors and playwrights, I feel it's our job to help nurture and encourage their ever-blossoming imagination.

What writers have had the most profound effect on your style?
I can't give Christopher Durang enough credit. His plays and words have inspired me more than I'll probably ever know. As he has grown and evolved with each play and skit, I've professionally (and personally) tried to do the same. While his plays are not always family friendly, there's an earnest bit of sweetness tucked away in each one them, along with a nugget or two of wisdom. Those are two elements I'm constantly trying to parrot when it comes to my own work.

What do you hope to achieve with this work?
I hope to give the audience exactly what they came for—a *Wizard of Oz* story, but I also hope to give them something more. By incorporating the Choose Your Own element, it was my goal to have parents and children work together and create a show (and experience) that's uniquely their own. Theatre is a teaching tool in so many ways, and it's my hope that this show allows all kinds of people from all over to put their differences aside, come together, and make something truly magical.

What were the biggest challenges involved in the writing of this play?
The Choose Your Own element was a bit of a beast. Often times I called her "Tanya" because she felt like she was her own entity, rather than a theatrical device. She caused me to have a few snags while attempting to map out the piece— "How will *this* affect *that*? How will *that* affect *this*?" things of that nature—but, once I stopped thinking of her as a hindrance, (and a horrible monster looming over my shoulder) and more of a fun new twist that I got to play with, everything just fell into place nicely and neatly.

What are the most common mistakes that occur in productions of your work?
Directors usually take my work too literally. Stage directions are merely my suggestions. I feel that when directors refuse to color outside the lines with my pieces, it makes them feel stiff and by-the-book. It's my hope that they have as much fun with the show as possible. Explore the piece, take it in different directions; try incorporating unique concepts into the overall feel of the show. Take your actors and audience to the moon and back if need be. I'm sure they'll be happy they took the journey.

What inspired you to become a playwright?
I would have to say that, from an early age, I've always known that I wanted to be a writer. There is just something about the story telling process that appeals to me. I first discovered playwriting when I was in the sixth grade and my parents took me to see a production of Elton John and Tim Rice's *Aida*. The minute the curtain went up, I was entranced. From that moment on, I knew that the theatre was going to play a significant role in my life.

How did you research the subject?
I read and re-read plenty of *Choose Your Own Adventures*, the R.L. Stein ones being my personal favorite. Though I'm personally not the biggest fan of his writing style, I found some of the "choices" to be quite inspired and they were a great help to me.

Are any characters modeled after real life or historical figures?
If you consider Judy Garland to be a historical figure (I do), then yes. A tad. The "Dorothy" in this script, while not a carbon copy of Judy's interpretation, has a few moments that are reminiscent of the portrayal she gave — specifically some of the word choices I made. Other than that, no, none of the

characters were modeled after anyone other than the descriptions found in Baum's text.

How was the first production different from the vision that you created in your mind?

It actually had a few more bells and whistles than I initially imaged. With most of my plays, I imagine these grandiose sets and costumes, but with this one, even my imagination seemed to be a shoestring budget. I didn't picture it having grandiose anything. And yet, when the play opened, and the curtains parted, I was shocked to see the outfits, the lights, and all the dazzling colors that were before me. The show came alive, both physically and aesthetically in a way I hadn't imagined. It's safe to say I was more than pleased with its final outcome.

About the Author

Tommy Jamerson was born in North Carolina and raised in Northwest Indiana. He has been writing plays for over ten years. He attended and graduated from Indiana State University, studying theatre, with a concentration in playwriting and directing. His children's plays, *Princess Pigface* and *The Big Bad Bullysaurus* (which took home Second Place at the National Association of Dramatic & Speech Arts Festival), were recently published by YouthPLAYS and have since received numerous productions around the country. His newest children's show, *Alice the Brave & Other Tales from Wonderland*, received its world premiere at Cassidy Park (Bogalusa, LA) to a crowd of one thousand theatre patrons. He is currently a graduate student at the University of New Orleans and resides in Caldwell (NJ) with his partner, Mark, and their dog, Darby. Website: www.tommyjamerson.com.

About YouthPLAYS

YouthPLAYS (www.youthplays.com) is a publisher of award-winning professional dramatists and talented new discoveries, each with an original theatrical voice, and all dedicated to expanding the vocabulary of theatre for young actors and audiences. On our website you'll find one-act and full-length plays and musicals for teen and pre-teen (and even college) actors, as well as duets and monologues for competition. Many of our authors' works have been widely produced at high schools and middle schools, youth theatres and other TYA companies, both amateur and professional, as well as at elementary schools, camps, churches and other institutions serving young audiences and/or actors worldwide. Most are intended for performance by young people, while some are intended for adult actors performing for young audiences.

YouthPLAYS was co-founded by professional playwrights Jonathan Dorf and Ed Shockley. It began merely as an additional outlet to market their own works, which included a substantial body of award-winning published and unpublished plays and musicals. Those interested in their published plays were directed to the respective publishers' websites, and unpublished plays were made available in electronic form. But when they saw the desperate need for material for young actors and audiences—coupled with their experience that numerous quality plays for young people weren't finding a home—they made the decision to represent the work of other playwrights as well. Dozens and dozens of authors are now members of the YouthPLAYS family, with scripts available both electronically and in traditional acting editions. We continue to grow as we look for exciting and challenging plays and musicals for young actors and audiences.

About ProduceaPlay.com

Let's put up a play! Great idea! But producing a play takes time, energy and knowledge. While finding the necessary time and energy is up to you, ProduceaPlay.com is a website designed to assist you with that third element: knowledge.

Created by YouthPLAYS' co-founders, Jonathan Dorf and Ed Shockley, ProduceaPlay.com serves as a resource for producers at all levels as it addresses the many facets of production. As Dorf and Shockley speak from their years of experience (as playwrights, producers, directors and more), they are joined by a group of award-winning theatre professionals and experienced teachers from the world of academic theatre, all making their expertise available for free in the hope of helping this and future generations of producers, whether it's at the school or university level, or in community or professional theatres.

The site is organized into a series of major topics, each of which has its own page that delves into the subject in detail, offering suggestions and links for further information. For example, Publicity covers everything from Publicizing Auditions to How to Use Social Media to Posters to whether it's worth hiring a publicist. Casting details Where to Find the Actors, How to Evaluate a Resume, Callbacks and even Dealing with Problem Actors. You'll find guidance on your Production Timeline, The Theater Space, Picking a Play, Budget, Contracts, Rehearsing the Play, The Program, House Management, Backstage, and many other important subjects.

The site is constantly under construction, so visit often for the latest insights on play producing, and let it help make your play production dreams a reality.

More from YouthPLAYS

The Big Bad Bullysaurus by Tommy Jamerson
Young Audiences. 40-45 minutes. 3 males, 2 females, 2 either.

When paleontologist Mark learns that his niece, Natalie, is being harassed by a local bully, he tells her the story of Ryan Rex Jr., a little dinosaur with a big bully problem of his own. With the help of Ryan's pals Terry Pterodactyl and Bronnie Brontosaurus, Ryan and Natalie both learn a lesson about friendship and the importance of forgiveness. A four-actor version is also available.

The Goodcheer Home for Broken Hearts by James Grob
Comic Melodrama. 95-105 minutes. 7-30+ females, 4-30+ males (14-40+ performers possible).

Audiences get to boo, hiss, cheer and sigh in this spoof of the classic American melodrama. As the villainous Severus C. Snackwell takes aim at the Goodcheer Home for Broken Hearts, the sweet and matronly Charity Goodcheer, the smart, beautiful and great smelling Shasta Bellflower and indeed the entire backwater town of Wetwater, can the strong and sincere but soft-witted Steele Manly stop his nefarious plot?

Outside the Box by Bradley Hayward
Dramedy. 25-35 minutes. 12 either.

Thinking outside the box isn't always easy, especially when the world requires you to live on the inside. Exhausted from cramming into corners where they do not fit, six teenagers turn things inside out by inviting others to see things from a whole new perspective—outside to a world where balloons change color, brooms become dance partners, and kites fly without a string.

Harry's Hotter at Twilight by Jonathan Dorf
Comedy. 90-100 minutes. 5-25+ males, 7-25+ females (12-50+ performers possible).

In this crazed mash-up parody of *Harry Potter* and *Twilight*—with cameos crashing in from *Lord of the Rings*, *Star Wars*, *Alice in Wonderland* and many other places—you'll encounter deli-owning vegetarians, invisible rabbits, magical carrot weapons, random lunatics, soothing offstage voices, evil gourmets and much more, as everyone's favorite wizards, vampires and werewolves battle to save miserable, gloomy Spork—and indeed the world—from certain destruction.

The Tea Servant by Ed Shockley
Drama. 30-35 minutes. 3+ males, 2+ females (5-25 performers possible).

Adapted from an anonymous Samurai legend, *The Tea Servant* is the tale of a serving girl whose impetuous princess is determined to travel alone to her lover. The servant dresses as a samurai to discourage robbers, but she is no fighter. When confronted on the road by a highwayman, the servant asks for time to deliver her mistress safe to the village and promises to return to duel. And when she does, her courage in facing death gains her far more than she could have imagined.

The Very Bad Girl Scouts by John P. McEneny
Comedy. 60-65 minutes. 10-16 females, 4-7 males (19-30 performers possible).

Grooselda's life is shattered when her family moves her from the mountainside German village of Schwalm-Eder to the cold hallways of Consumption Middle School in New Jersey. As she and her twin brother, Dagobert, navigate the complicated caste system that is middle school and try to fit in, their efforts will put them on a collision course with the most dangerous group of all: the Girl Scouts.

Made in the USA
Middletown, DE
21 January 2020